Vocabulary
Power Plus for
College and Career Readiness

LEVEL
TEN

By Daniel A. Reed

Edited by Paul Moliken

Prestwick House

P.O. Box 658 • Clayton, DE 19938
(800) 932-4593 • www.prestwickhouse.com

ISBN   978-1-62019-1439

Vocabulary
Power Plus for
College and Career Readiness

LEVEL
TEN

•Table of Contents•

Vocabulary Power Plus for College and Career Readiness

LEVEL TEN

·Introduction·

VOCABULARY POWER PLUS FOR COLLEGE AND CAREER READINESS combines classroom-tested vocabulary drills with reading and writing exercises designed to foster the English and language arts skills essential for college and career success, with the added advantage of successfully preparing students for both the Scholastic Assessment Test and the American College Testing assessment.

Although *Vocabulary Power Plus* is a proven resource for college-bound students, it is guaranteed to increase vocabulary, improve grammar, enhance writing, and boost critical reading skills for students at all levels of learning.

Critical Reading exercises include lengthy passages and detailed, evidence-based, two-part questions designed to promote understanding and eliminate multiple-choice guessing. We include SAT- and ACT-style grammar and writing exercises and have placed the vocabulary words in non-alphabetical sequence, distributed by part-of-speech.

Coupled with words-in-context exercises, inferences cultivate comprehensive word discernment by prompting students to create contexts for words, instead of simply memorizing definitions. Related words-in-context exercises forge connections among words, ensuring retention for both knowledge and fluency, and nuance exercises instill active inference habits to discern not just adequate words for contexts, but the best words in a specific context.

The writing exercises in *Vocabulary Power Plus* are process-oriented and adaptable to individual classroom lesson plans. Our rubrics combine the fundamentals of the essay-scoring criteria for both the SAT and ACT optional writing portions, with emphasis on organization, development, sentence formation, and word choice. This objective scoring opportunity helps students develop a concrete understanding of the writing process and develop a personal approach to punctual, reactive writing.

We hope that you find the *Vocabulary Power Plus for College and Career Readiness* series to be an effective tool for teaching new words, and an exceptional tool for preparing for assessments.

Strategies for Completing Activities

Roots, Prefixes, and Suffixes

A knowledge of roots, prefixes, and suffixes can give readers the ability to view unfamiliar words as mere puzzles that require only a few simple steps to solve. For the person interested in the history of words, this knowledge provides the ability to track word origin and evolution. For those who seek to improve vocabulary, the knowledge creates a sure and lifelong method; however, there are two points to remember:

1. Some words have evolved through usage, so present definitions might differ from what you infer through an examination of the roots and prefixes. The word *abstruse*, for example, contains the prefix *ab–* (away) and the root *trudere* (to thrust), and literally means "to thrust away." Today, *abstruse* is used to describe something that is hard to understand.

2. Certain roots do not apply to all words that use the same form. If you know that the root *vin* means "to conquer," then you would be correct in concluding that the word *invincible* means "incapable of being conquered"; however, if you tried to apply the same root meaning to *vindicate* or *vindictive*, you would be incorrect. When analyzing unfamiliar words, check for other possible roots if your inferred meaning does not fit the context.

Despite these considerations, a knowledge of roots and prefixes is one of the best ways to build a powerful vocabulary.

Critical Reading

Reading questions generally fall into several categories.

1. Identifying the main idea or the author's purpose. *What is this selection about?*

In some passages, the author's purpose will be easy to identify because the one or two ideas leap from the text; however, other passages might not be so easily analyzed, especially if they include convoluted sentences. Inverted sentences (subject at the end of the sentence) and elliptical sentences (words missing) will also increase the difficulty of the passages, but all these obstacles can be overcome if readers take one sentence at a time and recast it in their own words. Consider the following sentence:

> These writers either jot down their thoughts bit by bit, in short, ambiguous, and paradoxical sentences, which apparently mean much more than they say—of this kind of writing Schelling's treatises on natural philosophy are a splendid instance; or else they hold forth with a deluge of words and the most intolerable diffusiveness, as though no end of fuss were necessary to make the reader understand the deep meaning of their sentences, whereas it is some quite simple if not actually trivial idea, examples of which may be found in plenty in the popular works of Fichte, and the philosophical manuals of a hundred other miserable dunces.

If we edit out some of the words, the main point of this sentence is obvious.

> These writers either jot down their thoughts bit by bit, in short ambiguous, and paradoxical sentences, which apparently mean much more than they say—of this kind of writing Schelling's treatises on natural philosophy are a splendid instance; or else they hold forth with a deluge of words and the most intolerable diffusiveness, as though [it] end of fuss were necessary to make the reader understand the deep meaning of their sentences, whereas it is som[a] quite simple if not actually trivial idea, examples of which may be found in plenty in the popular works of Fichte, and the philosophical manuals of a hundred other miserable dunces.

Some sentences need only a few deletions for clarification, but others require major recasting and additions; they must be read carefully and put into the reader's own words.

> Some in their discourse desire rather commendation of wit, in being able to hold all arguments, than of judgment, in discerning what is true; as if it were a praise to know what might be said, and not what should be thought.

After studying it, a reader might recast the sentence as follows:

> In conversation, some people desire praise for their abilities to maintain the conversation rather than their abilities to identify what is true or false, as though it were better to sound good than to know what is truth or fiction.

2.   Identifying the stated or implied meaning. *What is the author stating or suggesting?*

The literal meaning of a text does not always correspond with the intended meaning. To understand a passage fully, readers must determine which meaning—if there is more than one—is the intended meaning of the passage. Consider the following sentence:

> If his notice was sought, an expression of courtesy and interest gleamed out upon his features; proving that there was light within him and that it was only the outward medium of the intellectual lamp that obstructed the rays in their passage.

Interpreted literally, this Nathaniel Hawthorne metaphor suggests that a light-generating lamp exists inside the human body. Since this is impossible, the reader must look to the metaphoric meaning of the passage to understand it properly. In the metaphor, Hawthorne refers to the human mind—consciousness—as a lamp that emits light, and other people cannot always see the lamp because the outside "medium"—the human body—sometimes blocks it.

3.   Identifying the tone or mood of the selection. *What feeling does the text evoke?*

To answer these types of questions, readers must look closely at individual words and their connotations; for example, the words *stubborn* and *firm* have almost the same definition, but a writer who describes a character as *stubborn* rather than *firm* is probably suggesting something negative about the character.

Vocabulary Power Plus for College and Career Readiness includes evidence-based follow-up questions in every critical reading lesson, as prescribed by the Partnership for Assessment of Readiness for College and Careers (PARCC) consortium, and will be used in the 2016 revision of the SAT. These questions prompt for the contextual evidence that students use to answer the primary questions.

Writing

The optional writing portions on the two major assessment tests allow approximately 30 minutes for the composition of a well-organized, fully developed essay. Writing a satisfactory essay in this limited time requires facility in determining a thesis, organizing ideas, and producing adequate examples to support the ideas.

These fundamentals are equally important for success on the Smarter Balanced Assessment Consortium ELA Performance Task, which includes a substantial essay writing assignment based on provided source texts.

Such a time-limited essay might lack the perfection and depth that weeks of proofreading and editing provide research papers. Process is undoubtedly of primary importance, but students must consider the time constraints of both reality and those of the assessments they elect to complete. Completion of the essay is just as important as organization, development, and language use.

The thesis, the organization of ideas, and the support make the framework of a good essay. Before the actual writing begins, writers must create a mental outline by establishing a thesis, or main idea, and one or more specific supporting ideas (the number of ideas will depend on the length and content of the essay). Supporting ideas should not be overcomplicated; they are simply ideas that justify or explain the thesis. The writer must introduce and explain each supporting idea, and the resultant supporting paragraph should answer the *Why?* or *Who cares?* questions that the thesis may evoke.

Once the thesis and supporting ideas are identified, writers must determine the order in which the ideas will appear in the essay. A good introduction usually explains the thesis and briefly introduces the supporting ideas. Explanation of the supporting ideas should follow, with each idea in its own paragraph. The final paragraph, the conclusion, usually restates the thesis or summarizes the main ideas of the essay.

Adhering to the mental outline when the writing begins will help the writer organize and develop the essay. Using the Organization and Development scoring guides to evaluate practice essays will help to reinforce the process skills. The Word Choice and Sentence Formation scoring guides will help to strengthen language skills—the vital counterpart to essay organization and development.

Vocabulary Power Plus for College and Career Readiness includes two styles of writing prompts. SAT-style writing prompts feature general subjects such as art, history, literature, or politics. ACT-style writing prompts involve subjects specifically relevant to high school students. Both styles of writing prompts require students to assume a point of view and support it with examples and reasoning.

Pronunciation Guide

a	—	track
ā	—	mate
ä	—	father
â	—	care
e	—	pet
ē	—	be
i	—	bit
ī	—	bite
o	—	job
ō	—	wrote
ô	—	port, **fought**
ōō	—	proof
ŏŏ	—	full
u	—	pun
ū	—	**you**
û	—	purr
ə	—	about, system, supper, circus
oi	—	toy
îr	—	steer

Word List

Lesson 1
abet
ardor
ascribe
coerce
divulge
dogmatic
extraneous
gregarious
insipid
jaundiced
meticulous
occlude
proclivity
rote
temerity

Lesson 2
anathema
audit
banter
castigate
disabuse
dither
docile
emaciated
gauche
heresy
ignominy
libation
motley
repine
restive

Lesson 3
avarice
bacchanalian
bastion
conflate
copious
extradite
furtive
irascible
jettison
maudlin
mercenary
mettle
ostracize
solvent
tackle

Lesson 4
appease
argot
augment
bigot
candid
chaos
despondent
expunge
jingoism
negligence
privation
protocol
redress
strident
toilsome

Lesson 5
adamant
clement
cliché
conscript
diffident
disparity
extol
impute
inexorable
opus
ostensible
prate
rancor
retinue
unfettered

Lesson 6
collate
condone
connoisseur
credence
cult
dilettante
enigma
enthrall
fetid
genteel
jaunty
nuance
officious
torpor
venal

Word List

Lesson 7
affront
ambivalent
concur
culmination
demagogue
demure
destitute
dilemma
erudite
intern
intrepid
lobby
rend
sardonic
transpose

Lesson 8
abate
abhor
austere
belie
decorum
dole
droll
duplicity
effigy
extrovert
gamut
glib
journeyman
propagate
protean

Lesson 9
collaborate
contrite
emulate
enhance
evoke
expatriate
frowzy
heinous
impeccable
impound
inane
magnanimous
postulate
sere
unctuous

Lesson 10
acrimony
balk
cajole
dour
expound
exult
feasible
fiasco
fluctuate
harry
incognito
inscrutable
lethargy
métier
omniscient

Lesson 11
affable
agrarian
arduous
avid
dolorous
epistle
explicit
formidable
gadfly
gargantuan
grandiloquent
grimace
harangue
humility
sycophant

Lesson 12
altercation
audacity
evince
exhort
expedient
galvanize
hue
hyperbole
implacable
incarcerate
incisive
lexicon
ominous
pertinent
sanction

Word List

Lesson 13
acquit
adulation
artful
barrister
bawdy
chastise
circumvent
culinary
deprecate
frugal
inert
jocose
latent
myriad
pernicious

Lesson 15
befuddle
chutzpah
complacent
connive
crass
fallacy
hypercritical
indiscreet
laudable
liege
noxious
odium
pandemonium
parsimonious
verbose

Lesson 17
abscond
agnostic
caustic
circumspect
exodus
penitent
raillery
renegade
repose
retribution
scourge
taciturn
terse
uncanny
vindicate

Lesson 14
amicable
bask
charlatan
enraptured
fickle
genial
hoax
juggernaut
levity
marital
mundane
naïve
nocturnal
novice
obstreperous

Lesson 16
linguistics
pique
plebeian
precocious
predatory
prowess
pugnacious
purloin
pusillanimous
quell
quixotic
rabble
rabid
raconteur
vindictive

Lesson 18
discordant
expedite
filibuster
impregnable
inherent
invective
irreverent
pithy
pristine
prodigal
subdued
subjugate
tenuous
torpid
xenophobia

Word List

Lesson 19	Lesson 20	Lesson 21
approbation	accolade	albeit
arbiter	belligerent	ancillary
archetype	demur	asinine
attrition	derivative	august
burgeon	dissident	autodidact
commensurate	fixed	behest
confluence	insouciant	conduit
coup	invidious	dossier
epicurean	limpid	indefatigable
mellifluous	proliferate	indiscretion
oeuvre	ruminate	martyr
secular	stipulate	osmosis
vacuous	tenet	philatelist
vagary	vigilant	picayune
verdant	zeitgeist	semblance

Lesson One

1. **divulge** (di vulj′) *v.* to tell; to reveal (as a secret)
The reporter was fired when she *divulged* information from a classified document.
syn: unveil; disclose   *ant: conceal*

2. **abet** (ə bet′) *v.* to assist or encourage, especially in wrongdoing
Jim refused to *abet* the criminal's escape by hiding him in the basement.
syn: promote; incite   *ant: impede; dissuade*

3. **ardor** (ar′ dr) *n.* an intense feeling of devotion or eagerness
The defending troops fought with *ardor* because the enemy would not be taking any prisoners.
syn: zeal   *ant: indifference*

4. **dogmatic** (dôg mat′ ik) *adj.* arrogant and stubborn about one's beliefs
Because of the professor's *dogmatic* approach, the students were afraid to ask questions.
syn: dictatorial   *ant: open-minded*

5. **insipid** (in sip′ id) *adj.* lacking flavor; dull; not at all stimulating
My mom wanted me to be an accountant, but I found the classes boring and *insipid*.
syn: flat; lifeless   *ant: challenging*

6. **proclivity** (prō kli′ və tē) *n.* a natural leaning or tendency
Abigail's *proclivity* for history led her to write a book on the founders of her home town.
syn: propensity; inclination   *ant: apathy*

7. **extraneous** (ek strā′ nē əs) *adj.* not essential; not constituting a vital part
The professor felt that the *extraneous* paragraph in the essay detracted from the more important information.
syn: irrelevant; superfluous   *ant: essential; critical*

8. **coerce** (kō ûrs′) *v.* to force by using pressure, intimidation, or threats
Jerry preferred basketball, but his father *coerced* him into playing football.
syn: compel

9. **jaundiced** (jôn′ dist) *adj.* prejudiced; hostile
Gabe had a *jaundiced* view of Iraq after losing his wife in the Gulf War.
syn: skeptical; cynical   *ant: believing; trusting*

10. **occlude** (ə klōōd′) *v.* to block the passage of
A large mass of clay *occluded* the water pipe, causing a dangerous rise in pressure.
syn: obstruct; impede   *ant: advance; assist*

11. **meticulous** (mi tik´ yə ləs) *adj.* extremely, sometimes excessively, careful about small details; precise
With *meticulous* care, he crafted a miniature dollhouse for his daughter.
syn: fastidious   *ant: sloppy*

12. **temerity** (tə mer´ i tē) *n.* recklessness; a foolish disregard of danger
I couldn't believe that Bret had the *temerity* to bungee jump over a lake full of alligators.
syn: audacity   *ant: prudence*

13. **rote** (rōt) *n.* a habitual, repetitive routine or procedure
Kristen memorized the piano sonata through *rote*, by practicing the song over and over until she could play it perfectly.

14. **ascribe** (ə skrīb´) *v.* to credit as to the cause or the source
The carpenter *ascribed* the rotten floorboards to a leaky roof.
syn: attribute; impute

15. **gregarious** (gri gâr´ ē əs) *adj.* sociable; fond of the company of others
Just before he was diagnosed with clinical depression, Raji went from being *gregarious* to being antisocial.
syn: genial; friendly   *ant: reclusive*

Exercise I

Words in Context

From the list below, supply the words needed to complete the paragraph. Some words will not be used.

~~divulge~~   ~~abet~~   ~~temerity~~   ~~insipid~~
~~gregarious~~   ~~coerce~~   ~~jaundiced~~

1. Jasmine had thought that her irresponsible days of **temerity** were far behind her until Kayla showed up at her door. After only three days of freedom from the county correctional facility, Kayla had begun her old scheming again. She went to the house to **coerce** Jasmine into helping her move a truckload of stolen goods to another state—an easy job, she claimed, and virtually no risk. It would even be fun, she claimed.

    "Let me get this straight. You've been out of jail for three days, and you already want me to **abet** you in your scheme to commit a crime? Are you crazy?"

    Jasmine still had a[n] **jaundiced** attitude toward her sister because Kayla, prior to her first sentence, "borrowed" Jasmine's car for a robbery and nearly got Jasmine arrested as a result.

    "Sorry, Kayla, but I'm quite happy with my **insipid**, uneventful life. Please leave, and don't come back."

From the list below, supply the words needed to complete the paragraph. Some words will not be used.

~~dogmatic~~   ~~abet~~   ~~gregarious~~   ~~divulge~~
~~extraneous~~   ~~coerce~~   ~~meticulous~~

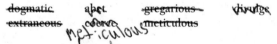

2. Mr. Knight learned the **dogmatic** art of watchmaking during a three-year stay in Switzerland more than forty years ago. Since that time, he has spent countless evenings in his basement workshop assembling the tiny, complex machines. As a[n] **meticulous** grandfather, Mr. Knight often invites his grandchildren to his shop, where they watch with amazement through a large magnifying glass and see a newly assembled pocket watch tick for the first time.

    "Watches are such perfect machines; there's no room for **extraneous** parts or over-engineering. And then, to see such a tiny machine operate under its own power— it amazes me every time."

    When asked about his thoughts on the mass production techniques of modern watches, Knight revealed his **extraneous** belief that Old World skills made watches much more valuable.

"Oh, yes, the new watches are inexpensive and readily available, which fills the practical need, but they lack the sentiment and the many hours of craftsmanship that should go into a fine piece of jewelry."

"These watches," he says as he points to a sparkling display cabinet, "have character."

Mr. Knight hopes someday to *divulge* the many secrets of his trade to his youngest grandson, who can then carry on the family tradition for years to come.

From the list below, supply the words needed to complete the paragraph. Some words will not be used.

ardor	jaundiced	proclivity	divulge
rote	ascribe	occlude	

3. Many spectators _____ Chris's ability to natural talent, but Chris is the first to claim that years of _____ were necessary to develop the skill to strike pennies thrown into the air with his arrows. A sportsman and Olympic hopeful, Chris discovered his _____ for archery at the early age of three. The secret of his success, he claims, is to compete with the same level of _____ at every event, no matter how small the prize, and to never allow previous victories to _____ the vision of your immediate goal.

Exercise II

Sentence Completion

Complete the sentence in a way that shows you understand the meaning of the italicized vocabulary word.

1. Rhea lacks *temerity*, so she definitely would not… Hang glide

2. Because the tall hedge *occluded* the pretty view from the porch, Clayton decided to… get rid of it.

3. Hikers should avoid packing *extraneous* gear because… It can be heavy

4. History *ascribes* the cause of the American Revolution to… America

5. A *jaundiced* judge might not be able to… Render a verdict

6. Anna's *meticulous* cleaning habits ensure that her room is always… Clean

7. I made my psychiatrist promise not to *divulge* any… details

8. My *dogmatic* English teacher refused to… let me wear my hood

9. Mel thinks musicals are *insipid*, so when I asked her to see *Miss Saigon* with me, she… Said no

10. Though they represented the minority opinion, the protesters argued with such *ardor* that they... won

11. After two weeks, Jess was already sick of the *rote* involved in...
    exercise

12. Lisa decided to *abet* the bank robber by...
    being the getaway driver

13. I've never been *gregarious*, so at parties I tend to...
    not be very social

14. My boss tried to *coerce* me into attending the company picnic by...
    giving me a bonus

15. Someone who has a *proclivity* for gardening might...
    garden

Exercise III

Roots, Prefixes, and Suffixes

Study the entries and answer the questions that follow.

The prefix *mal–* means "bad" or "evil."
The root *bene* means "good."
The root *dict* means "to speak."
The root *vol* means "to wish."
The root *fact* means "making, doing"; *factor* means "one who does."

1. Using *literal* translations as guidance, define the following words without using a dictionary:

    A. malevolent   D. benevolent
    B. malediction   E. benediction
    C. malefactor   F. benefactor

2. After a biopsy, tumors are generally labeled _____ or _____.

3. List as many other related words as you can that begin with either *mal–* or *bene*.

Exercise IV

Inference

Complete the sentence by inferring information about the italicized word from its context.

1. Since Dad had a handful of *extraneous* parts after assembling Kyle's bicycle, Kyle might…

2. If students complain about a teacher's *insipid* lectures, the teacher should…

3. Martin's refusal to *divulge* the location of the military base probably means that the base is…

Exercise V

Writing

Here is a writing prompt similar to the one you will find on the writing portion of an assessment test.

Plan and write an essay based on the following statement:

> Happiness is an imaginary condition, formerly often attributed by the living to the dead, now usually attributed by adults to children, and by children to adults.
>
> –Thomas Szasz
> *The Second Sin* (1973)

Assignment: Do you agree or disagree with Szasz's view that happiness is merely imaginary? Write an essay in which you support or refute Szasz's position. Be certain to support your point with evidence from your own reading, classroom studies, and experience.

Thesis: Write a *one-sentence* response to the above assignment. Make certain this single sentence offers a clear statement of your position.

Example: Happiness is not imaginary, but it is an elusive condition because unhappy people see only the happiness of others.

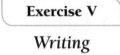

Happines is not imaginary, but
it is a feeling we have when something
that pleases us

Organizational Plan: List at least three subtopics you will use to support your main idea. This list is your outline.

1. _____

2. _____

3. _____

Draft: Following your outline, write a good first draft of your essay. Remember to support all your points with examples, facts, references to reading, etc.

Review and Revise: Exchange essays with a classmate. Using the scoring guide for Organization on page 257, score your partner's essay (while he or she scores yours). Focus on the organizational plan and the use of language conventions. If necessary, rewrite your essay to improve the organizational plan and/or your use of language.

Exercise VI

English Practice

Identifying Sentence Errors

Identify the grammatical error in each of the following sentences. If the sentence contains no error, select answer choice E.

1. If the alarm had gone off earlier, more people could of escaped before the
                    (A)   (B)   (C)
    building collapsed.   No error
              (D)   (E)

2. The principals of good sportsmanship demand that we cheer the
            (A)   (B)
    achievements of both teams.   No error
        (C)   (D)   (E)

3. Neither Kelley nor Larry are planning to attend the conference in November.
                (A)   (B)   (C)   (D)
    No error
     (E)

4. The boat sailed under the bridge and was rocking from the waves.   No error
        (A)   (B)   (C)   (D)   (E)

5. There were less people on that cruise than usual because of the weather. No error
        (A)   (B)   (C)   (D)   (E)

Improving Sentences

The underlined portion of each sentence below contains some flaw. Select the answer choice that best corrects the flaw.

6. <u>Lori said to her mother that she needed to buy some new clothes</u>.
   A. Lori said to her mother that Lori needed to buy some new clothes.
   B. Lori said to her mother that her mother needed to buy some new clothes.
   C. Lori's mom wanted to buy herself some new clothes.
   D. Lori said that her mother needed to buy some new clothes.
   E. Lori said to her mother that, "She needs to buy some new clothes."

7. <u>Softened by the boiling water, Ramona mashed the potatoes</u>.
   A. Ramona, softened by the boiling water, mashed the potatoes.
   B. Ramona mashed the potatoes that were softened by the boiling water.
   C. Ramona mashed the softened potatoes by the boiling water.
   D. The potatoes softened by the boiling water Ramona mashed.
   E. The potatoes that were softened by the boiling water were mashed by Ramona.

8. The founders of the United States selected the colors of the flag for their symbolism: white for the purity of the new nation's aspirations, <u>red to stand for the blood</u> shed gaining and keeping freedom, and blue for loyalty.
   A. red, which stands for the blood,
   B. red that stands for the blood
   C. red for the blood
   D. red, the color of blood
   E. red like the blood

9. After several attempts to call, Doug still couldn't <u>get through the line was</u> always busy.
   A. get through, the line was
   B. get through—the line was
   C. get through although the line was
   D. get through, and the line was
   E. get through because the line was

10. Because she was on a diet, <u>Naomi only ate three light meals a day</u>.
    A. only Naomi ate three light meals a day.
    B. Naomi ate only three light meals a day.
    C. Naomi ate three light meals a day only.
    D. Naomi easily ate three light meals a day.
    E. only three light meals a day were eaten by Naomi.

Vocabulary
Power Plus for
College and Career Readiness

LEVEL

Lesson Two

1. **disabuse** (dis ə byo͞os´) *v.* to free someone from believing something false
   Pam felt it was time to *disabuse* her son of his belief in the tooth fairy.
   syn: enlighten; inform   *ant: lie; misinform*

2. **heresy** (her´ i sē) *n.* the act of holding a belief that goes against established
   doctrine
   During the Inquisition, those found guilty of *heresy* were sometimes burned at the
   stake.
   ant: orthodoxy

3. **audit** (ô´ dit) *v.* to check the accuracy of financial accounts and records
   When Sienna is ready to graduate, the university will *audit* her records to verify that
   she took all the required classes.
   syn: inspect; examine

4. **motley** (mot´ lē) *adj.* made up of dissimilar parts; being of many colors
   The international clown convention was a *motley* sight in the otherwise dull
   exhibition center.
   syn: varied   *ant: uniform; homogeneous;*
                                          similar

5. **libation** (lī bā´ shən) *n.* a drink, especially an alcoholic one
   When we visited the vineyard, we were offered a small *libation* at the end of our tour.
   syn: intoxicant

6. **docile** (dos´ əl) *adj.* easy to teach or manage; obedient
   The poodle, usually *docile*, went mad and attacked its owner.
   syn: submissive; compliant   *ant: unmanageable; willful*

7. **restive** (res´ tiv) *adj.* restless and impatient
   Two *restive* students sat in chairs outside the principal's office waiting to be called
   inside.
   syn: edgy; jumpy   *ant: relaxed; calm*

8. **banter** (ban´ tər) *n.* teasing; playful conversation
   At the reunion, Ruth enjoyed listening to the *banter* of her husband and his old
   college roommate.
   syn: joshing; badinage; raillery   *ant: vituperation*

9. **castigate** (kas´ ti gāt) *v.* to criticize or punish severely
   The parson *castigated* the boy for noisily chewing gum in church.
   syn: reprimand; chastise; scold   *ant: praise*

10. **anathema** (ə nath´ ə mə)   *n.*   a hated, repellant person or thing
    Cannibalism is *anathema* to almost every society on the planet.
    syn: abhorration; detestation   *ant: beloved*

11. **gauche** (gōsh)   *adj.*   lacking social graces; tactless
    Some people use a fork to eat pizza because they think it is *gauche* to use their fingers.
    syn: awkward   *ant: graceful*

12. **ignominy** (ig´ nə min ē)   *n.*   public shame, disgrace, or dishonor
    The mayor fell from public acclaim to complete *ignominy* in a week when her cocaine habit was discovered.
    syn: disgrace; infamy   *ant: renown; eminence; repute*

13. **dither** (di´ thər)   *v.*   to hesitate nervously
    When asked if he had completed his homework assignment, Luke *dithered*, knowing that he had forgotten about it.
    syn: vacillate; waver   *ant: settle; conclude*

14. **emaciated** (i mā´ shē āt ed)   *adj.*   extremely thin; wasted away
    Dead from starvation, the *emaciated* prisoner was buried in the camp cemetery.
    syn: withered   *ant: plump; fattened*

15. **repine** (rə pīn´)   *v.*   to be discontent as though yearning for something; to complain
    Nathan *repined* loudly in his room after getting grounded for picking on his sister.
    syn: grumble; fret

Exercise I

Words in Context

From the list below, supply the words needed to complete the paragraph. Some words will not be used.

gauche	castigate	heresy	banter
anathema	ignominy	emaciated	

1. After five years of starvation and torture, the *anathem* Kwame prayed for death. Hope was a foreign concept to him now; he no longer remembered what it was like to live in the sunlight. When he tried to remember, all he could visualize were the three years of humiliating *ignomin* that preceded his incarceration. He couldn't even remember the faces of his wife and children anymore.

    The whole thing began when Kwame's brother, a schoolteacher, wrote a letter to a nonprofit agency in the United States to appeal for educational funds. The letter was intercepted, and Sirajul's agents brought the letter to Sirajul himself. The mad dictator declared that any letter that portrayed his reign in a bad light was total *heresy*. Kwame's brother was executed, and then, to make a point, Sirajul *castigat* and imprisoned the entire family. While dictators like Sirajul were a[n] *gauche* to virtually anyone in the civilized world, few people had the means to stop them.

From the list below, supply the words needed to complete the paragraph. Some words will not be used.

gauche	motley	emaciated	libation
banter	docile	heresy	

2. The actors gathered in the banquet room after the closing night of the hit play. Sounds of lighthearted *banter* filled the room; some of the more *docile* performers thought nothing of picking two or more cold *libations* at a time from the trays of the servers. The players were still in costumes depicting various cultures and historic eras, and arriving guests paused at the door to take in the *gauche* sight. The company had just completed its twentieth and final show of a successful run, and the performers were happy to relax. The spirited staff, laughing and carousing, became *emancated* only when the director raised her hands to quiet the room. Anticipating her words of encouragement, none of the actors suspected that she was about to announce her retirement.

From the list below, supply the words needed to complete the paragraph. Some words will not be used.

anathema	**restive**	**audit**	**disabuse**
gauche	—dither—	—repine—	

3. Just minutes after an employee *disabused* Skylar of the belief that the investment firm was not in danger as a result of a former employee's criminal charges, FBI agents arrived to *audit* accounts linked to the investigation. The *restive* accountants paced nervously, wondering whether or not they had accidentally participated in a scam. Skylar *dithered* when the special agent asked questions that she had never considered, and she *repined* the day she hired Bernard, the man who had bilked investors of over $20 million.

Exercise II

Sentence Completion

Complete the sentence in a way that shows you understand the meaning of the italicized vocabulary word.

1. The *emaciated* girl looked as if she had not… *eaten*

2. A traditional *libation* at weddings and New Year's Eve parties is… *wine*

3. The old man often *repines* as he remembers… *the war*

4. If someone you have a crush on engages in extended *banter* with you, you might conclude… *with laughing*

5. When the teacher returned to find a *docile* class, he knew that…
    Something was wrong

6. By the way the soloist *dithered*, the audience could tell…
    She was playing the wrong note's

7. The Spanish Inquisition charged don Torino with *heresy* for allegedly…
    Starting a rebellion

8. One thing that is *anathema* to our society is…
    Social media

9. If Sarita tells me that her new dress is *motley*, I can assume that it is…
    colorful

10. The students are always *restive* when…
    A Quiz is handed out

11. A supervisor might *castigate* an employee if…
    He messes up

12. The television evangelist faced *ignominy* when the public…
    started talking

13. Jodi *audits* the concession stand money every week to make sure that…

She has the right amount

14. Tim *disabused* Roger of…

Saying he has guilty

15. At a wedding, it might be considered *gauche* if you…

eat the cake before it's time.

Exercise III

Roots, Prefixes, and Suffixes

Study the entries and answer the questions that follow.

The root *anthro* means "man."
The suffix *–ology* means "study of."
The root *theo* means "god" or "religion."
The suffix *–oid* means "having the shape of."
The root *morph* means "shape."
The prefix *a–* means "not."
The suffix *–cracy* means "government by."

1. Using *literal* translations as guidance, define the following words without using a dictionary:

   A. anthropology   D. anthropomorphic
   B. theology   E. atheism
   C. anthropoid   F. theocracy

2. What is studied in the science of *sociology*?

3. List as many words as you can think of that contain either *anthro* or *theo* or end in *–ology*.

Exercise IV

Inference

Complete the sentence by inferring information about the italicized word from its context.

1. If Grace complained that Jeremy was *gauche* on the dance floor, you might assume that Jeremy was…

2. A *docile* dog is probably easier to train than an aggressive dog because…

3. When offered food for the first time in weeks, the *emaciated* castaway probably…

Exercise V

Critical Reading

Below is a reading passage followed by several multiple-choice questions. Carefully read the passage and choose the best answer for each of the questions.

H. G. Wells, author of The Invisible Man *and* The Time Machine, *was also very interested in history. The following passage, "Primitive Thought," is adapted from Wells's* A Short History of the World. *In it, Wells speculates on the origins of human thought and religion.*

How did it feel to be alive in the early days of the human adventure? How did men and women think and what did they think in those remote days four hundred centuries ago? Those were days long before the written record of any human impressions, and we are left almost entirely to inference and guesswork in our answers to these questions.

5   Primitive humans probably thought very much as a child thinks. They conjured up images or images presented themselves to their minds, and they acted in accordance with the emotions these pictures aroused. So a child or an uneducated person does today. Systematic thinking is apparently a comparatively late development in human experience; it has not played any great part in human life until within the last three thousand years. And even today those who really

10   control and order their thoughts are a small minority of humankind. Most of the world still lives by imagination and passion.

Probably the earliest human societies were small family groups. Just as the flocks and herds of the earlier mammals arose out of families which remained together and multiplied, so probably did the earliest human tribes. But before this could happen, a certain restraint upon the primitive

15   egotisms of the individual had to be established. The fear of the father and respect for the mother had to be extended into adult life, and the natural jealousy of the old man of the group for the younger males as they grew up had to be mitigated. Human social life grew up out of the reaction between the instinct of the young to go off by themselves as they grew up, on the one hand, and the dangers and disadvantages of separation on the other.

20   Some writers would have us believe that respect and fear of the Old Man and the emotional reaction of the primitive to older protective women, exaggerated in dreams and enriched by imagination, played a large part in the beginnings of primitive religion and in the conception of gods and goddesses. Associated with this respect for powerful or helpful personalities was a dread and exaltation of such personages after their deaths, due to their reappearance in dreams.

25   It was easy to believe they were not truly dead but only fantastically transferred to a remoteness of greater power.

The dreams, imaginations, and fears of a child are far more vivid and real than those of a modern adult, and primitive humans were always somewhat like children. They were nearer to the animals also, and could suppose these animals to have motives and reactions like their own.
30 They could imagine animal helpers, animal enemies, animal gods. One needs only to have been an imaginative child oneself to realize again how important, significant, portentous or kind strangely shaped rocks, lumps of wood, exceptional trees, or the like may have appeared to the men of the Old Stone Age, and how dream and fancy would create stories and legends about such things that would become credible as they were told. Some of these stories would be good enough to
35 remember and tell again. The women would tell them to the children and so establish a tradition. To this day most imaginative children invent stories in which some favourite doll or animal or some fantastic being figures as the hero, and primitive storytellers probably did the same—with a much stronger disposition to believe his hero real.

At the same time, primitive humans were not very critical in their associations of cause with
40 effect; they very easily connected an effect with something quite wrong as its cause. "You do so and so," they said, "and so and so happens." You give a child a poisonous berry and it dies. You eat the heart of a valiant enemy and you become strong. There we have two bits of cause and effect association, one true one false. We call the system of cause and effect in the mind of a primitive, Fetish; but Fetish is simply primitive science. It differs from modern science in that it is totally
45 unsystematic and uncritical and so more frequently wrong.

In many cases other erroneous ideas were soon **disabused** by experience; but there was a large series of issues of very great importance to primitive humans, where they sought persistently for causes and found explanations that were wrong but not sufficiently wrong nor so obviously wrong as to be detected. It was a matter of great importance to them that game should
50 be abundant or fish plentiful and easily caught, and no doubt they tried and believed in a thousand **motley** charms, incantations and omens to determine these desirable results. Another great concern of his was illness and death. Occasionally infections crept through the land and people died of them. Occasionally people were stricken by illness and died or were enfeebled without any manifest cause. Such **castigation** for unidentified acts of **heresy** must have given the hasty,
55 emotional, primitive mind much feverish exercise. Dreams and fantastic guesses made primitive people blame this, or appeal for help to that person, or beast, or thing.

Quite early in the little human tribe, older, steadier minds who shared the fears and the imaginations, but who were a little more forceful than the others must have asserted themselves, to advise, to prescribe, to command. This they declared unlucky and that imperative, this an
60 omen of good and that an omen of evil. The expert in Fetish, the Medicine Man, was the first priest. He exhorted, he interpreted dreams, he warned, he performed the complicated hocus pocus that brought luck or averted calamity. Primitive religion was not so much what we now call religion as practice and observance, and the early priest dictated what was indeed an arbitrary primitive practical science.

1A. According to lines 10-11, people who think systematically
    A. determine the course of human progression.
    B. think with childlike minds.
    C. are outnumbered by people driven by emotion.
    D. composed a large portion of early civilization.
    E. are the modern equivalent of medicine men.

1B. Which one of the following elements is a characteristic of systematic thought, according to paragraph 2?
    A. passion
    B. imagery
    C. control
    D. jealousy
    E. emotion

2A. The overall tone of this passage is
  A. thoughtful and speculative.
  B. scholarly and authoritative.
  C. facetious and entertaining.
  D. esoteric and thoughtful.
  E. strident and conciliatory.

2B. Choose the line from the passage that best supports your answer to question 2A.
  A. "Probably the earliest human societies were small family groups."
  B. "This they declared unlucky and that imperative, this an omen of good and that an omen of evil."
  C. "They could imagine animal helpers, animal enemies, animal gods."
  D. "There we have two bits of cause and effect association, one true one false."
  E. "…we are left almost entirely to inference and guesswork in our answers to these questions."

3A. As used in line 15, the word *egotism* most nearly means
  A. criminal temptation.
  B. vanity.
  C. instability.
  D. unwarranted fear.
  E. inclination.

3B. Who does the author suggest is most prone to acting on his or her *egotism*?
  A. young men
  B. mothers
  C. members of families
  D. all humans
  E. older people

4A. Which choice best states the psychological conflict that guided human social interaction?
  A. fear of father versus respect for mother
  B. dangers of separation versus desire to be independent
  C. jealousy of elders versus fear of separation
  D. instinct to be independent versus jealousy of larger families
  E. desires to remain together versus respect for father

4B. Choose the phrase that best supports your answer to question 4A.
  A. Individuals had to overcome their desire to leave their families.
  B. Human beings do not form herds, unlike lower orders of mammals.
  C. Flocks cannot form until families spread out.
  D. Fear and respect cannot be elements of advanced societies.
  E. Individuals had to overcome their desire to stay with their families.

5A. As it is used in line 33, the word *fancy* most nearly means
   A. embellished.
   B. elegant.
   C. imagination.
   D. fond.
   E. anxious.

5B. Which words in the context of *fancy* are the best clues to its meaning?
   A. remember, again
   B. rocks, trees
   C. dream, create
   D. important, Stone Age
   E. children, tradition

6A. Which of the following is the best paraphrase of the sentence "…Fetish is simply primitive science" (line 44)?
   A. Science is not based on superstition.
   B. The science of fetishism is simple and, therefore, primitive.
   C. The original word for science was *fetish*.
   D. The roots of modern science lie in superstition.
   E. Fetish and superstition are primitive.

6B. Choose the scenario that is analogous to the author's example of the false logic of primitive science.
   A. A man is always seen wearing brown shoes; therefore, he likes brown shoes.
   B. A poor decision leads to a bad outcome, while a wise decision provides rewards.
   C. Only one out of every two people survive a trek across the desert; therefore, only half the desert travelers succeed.
   D. A fisherman catches more fish in the morning than in the evening, so he prefers to fish in the morning.
   E. A canary dies just as a doorbell rings; therefore, bell sounds are fatal to canaries.

7A. According to paragraph 8, how did primitive Medicine Men attain their status?
   A. They professed more knowledge and power than others in their tribe.
   B. They rose in status by instilling fear in others.
   C. The oldest man in the tribe was chosen as Medicine Man.
   D. The strongest warrior in the tribe was chosen as Medicine Man.
   E. The Medicine Man was revealed in a tribal dream.

7B. Which descriptive phrase in the paragraph best supports your answer to question 7A?
   A. "he interpreted dreams, he warned"
   B. "more forceful than the others…The expert in Fetish"
   C. "He exhorted…he performed"
   D. "shared the fears and the imaginations"
   E. "brought luck or averted calamity"

8A. Which choice is not a phase in the development of primitive science and religion, according to the author?
   A. Primitive people observed events and their apparent causes.
   B. Primitive people attempted to find the means to control the forces that affected their lives.
   C. Primitive people attributed power to other people, animals, and objects.
   D. Primitive people elected a priest from among their tribal members.
   E. Primitive people developed ritual from behavior they thought would protect them from harm.

8B. Choose the answer that best describes how primitive humans became leaders, as supposed by the author.
   A. They outlived their enemies.
   B. They took charge on their own.
   C. They had prophetic visions.
   D. Tribal councils elected them.
   E. They reached the required age.

9A. According to this passage, primitive religion was the precursor to
   A. tribal belief systems.
   B. superstition.
   C. practical science.
   D. respect for elders.
   E. a rapid increase in population.

9B. The foundation of science, as it is described in lines 39-45, involves
   A. defending knowledge.
   B. reacting to information gathered.
   C. designating priests to bring luck.
   D. practicing prescribed rituals.
   E. observing the rules set by "steadier minds."

10A. This passage would most likely be found in
   A. a popular science magazine.
   B. an introductory history book.
   C. an encyclopedia of world religion.
   D. a book of ancient mythology.
   E. a doctoral dissertation.

10B. The title of the essay is "Primitive Thought." Choose the most appropriate subtitle for the passage.
   A. The Medicine Man
   B. How Families Began
   C. The Origins of Science
   D. Ancient Society Building
   E. Ancient Superstitions

Lesson Three

1. **irascible** (i ras´ ə bəl) *adj.* easily angered
   We walk on eggshells around Marty because he is so *irascible*.
   syn: irritable; ill-tempered　　　　　　　　　*ant: easygoing*

2. **bacchanalian** (bak ə nāl´ yən) *adj.* wild and drunken
   Adam paid for his *bacchanalian* weekend when he flunked the exam on Monday.
   　　　　　　　　　　　　　　　　　　　ant: restrained

3. **maudlin** (môd´ lin) *adj.* foolishly sentimental; ridiculously emotional
   The scam artist put forth a *maudlin* display of outrage when his victims accused him of stealing their money.
   syn: mushy; hokey　　　　　　　　　　*ant: stoic*

4. **extradite** (ek´ strə dīt) *v.* to turn over or deliver to the legal jurisdiction of another government or authority
   After two months of incarceration in Sacramento, the suspect was *extradited* to Florida.
   syn: deport

5. **furtive** (fûr´ tiv) *adj.* stealthy; secretive
   Not wanting to be rude, Jean cast only a *furtive* glance at the man's prominent scar.
   syn: surreptitious; sneaky　　　　　　　　*ant: overt*

6. **mettle** (me´ təl) *n.* courage and determination
   The secret mission behind enemy lines would require soldiers who have *mettle* because many probably wouldn't be coming back.
   syn: nerve; spirit　　　　　　　　　*ant: cowardice; fear*

7. **conflate** (kən flāt´) *v.* to combine into one
   When Henry wrote about cavemen hunting dinosaurs, his teacher explained that he had *conflated* two ideas.
   syn: fuse; merge　　　　　　　　　　*ant: divide; split*

8. **mercenary** (mûr´ sə ner ē) *n.* a professional soldier hired by a foreign army
   Though American by birth, the *mercenary* fought for France.
   　　　　　　　　　　　　　　　　　　ant: volunteer

9. **bastion** (bas´ chən) *n.* a strong defense or fort (or something likened to it)
   The United States has been called the *bastion* of democracy.
   syn: stronghold

10. **avarice**   (av´ ə ris)   *n.*   greed; desire for wealth
    He became a doctor, not to save lives, but to appease his *avarice*.
    syn: acquisitiveness   *ant: largesse*

11. **jettison**   (jet´ i sən)   *v.*   to cast overboard; to discard
    The passengers quickly *jettisoned* the heavy cargo from the damaged plane.
    syn: deploy; throw away   *ant: retain*

12. **solvent**   (sol´ vənt)   *adj.*   able to pay all debts and financial obligations
    The owner of the company must keep the business *solvent* or else vendors will refuse
    to do business with him.

13. **ostracize**   (os´ trə sīz)   *v.*   to banish; to shut out from a group or society by
       common consent
    The strict religious community *ostracized* Eli when he married a woman of another
    faith.
    syn: exile   *ant: accept*

14. **tackle**   (ta´ kəl)   *n.*   the equipment for a specific activity
    At the dive shop, you can rent *tackle* for today's trip to Half Moon Cove.
    syn: gear; tools

15. **copious**   (kō´ pē əs)   *adj.*   numerous; large in quantity
    It is good to drink a *copious* amount of water before and after working out.
    syn: profuse; abundant   *ant: sparse*

Exercise I

Words in Context

From the list below, supply the words needed to complete the paragraph. Some words will not be used.

extradite	ostracize	furtive	avarice
mercenary	bacchanalian	bastion	copious

1. Hired to combat an increase in drug trafficking, the _mercenary_ silently crawled through the fence line of the kingpin's plantation and found a good hiding place. For two days, Manco sat in the patch and observed the mansion—supposedly an impenetrable _bastion_ from which the criminal operated his international cartel. Manco was relieved to see that the rumors were false; the kingpin's _bacchanalian_ lifestyle of nightly parties would make Manco's job simple because of the noise and inadequate light beyond the cocktail area. After a[n] _copious_ infiltration of the mansion, Manco would have an easy time arresting the man, handcuffing him, sneaking him out, and then _extraditing_ him to the States, where he would face trial on a number of charges. The drug lord was about to become a victim of his own _avarice_; had he kept his illegal business small and untraceable, no one would have hired Manco to deal with him.

From the list below, supply the words needed to complete the paragraph. Some words will not be used.

bastion	jettison	irascible	avarice	ostracize

2. Isabel's _irascible_ personality had gotten her into trouble before, but never as much as it did now. In reaction to her outburst during the assembly, Isabel's class _ostracized_ her. Classmates would not sit next to Isabel, let alone speak to her. If her disruption had happened on a ship, Isabel thought, the passengers might have _jettison_ her over the side.

From the list below, supply the words needed to complete the paragraph. Some words will not be used.

solvent	mercenary	mettle	irascible
tackle	conflate	maudlin	

3. The company lost money on their latest _conflate_ advertisement that equated laundry detergent to a parent's love. Barely _solvent_, the company needed a new CEO who had the _mettle_ to make difficult changes while juggling the board's list of demands. The directors _irascible_ their requirements for the new recruit to include both lengthy experience and proven success, the _mercenary_ that would enable the new CEO to turn the company around.

Exercise II

Sentence Completion

Complete the sentence in a way that shows you understand the meaning of the italicized vocabulary word.

1. The child's *maudlin* crying failed to convince her mom to… *give her candy*

2. A criminal might be *extradited* to her home state for… *Ime gration*

3. After a *bacchanalian* weekend, Ethan felt… *hung over*

4. It is a burden to have an *irascible* supervisor because… *they yell*

5. Samantha was not sure if she had the *mettle* to… *do It*

6. The *mercenary* received no payment and refused to… *continue the Job*

7. The failing company had to *jettison* its… *Space People*

8. I made a mistake and *conflated* football and… *Soccer*

9. The cliquish teens *ostracized* Raymond from their group because… *He was weird*

10. If the new boss fails to make the company *solvent*, the workers will… *But yet*

11. If I allow *avarice* to guide my career, I might choose to… *be a doctor*

12. There was *copious* weeping whenever… *Jimmy died*

13. A church might be called a *bastion* of… *faith*

14. One might want to be especially *furtive* when… *here hiding Something*

15. You'll need to get the right *tackle* before you… *go fishing*

Exercise III

Roots, Prefixes, and Suffixes

Study the entries and answer the questions that follow.

The root *aud* means "hear."
The root *herb* means "grass, weed."
The roots *cis* and *cide* mean "cut" or "kill."
The roots *vis* and *vid* mean "see."
The suffixes *–ible* and *–able* mean "able."
The prefix *in–* means "into."

1. Using *literal* translations as guidance, define the following words without using a dictionary:

    A. audible   D. vista
    B. visionary   E. auditory
    C. herbicide   F. incision

2. The root *sui* in the word *suicide* probably means _____.

3. List as many words as you can that have the roots *aud* and *vid* in them.

4. Write one example of an *incisive* comment.

5. List as many words as you can that end in *–cide*.

Exercise IV

Inference

Complete the sentence by inferring information about the italicized word from its context.

1. If the king's *avarice* gets out of control, he might decide to…

2. Even a little good-humored teasing might cause the *irascible* Cary to…

3. If his promised wages do not arrive before the battle, the *mercenary* will probably…

Exercise V

Writing

Here is a writing prompt similar to the one you will find on the writing portion of an assessment test.

Plan and write an essay based on the following statement:

> One indication of good literature is that it "rings true," which means it touches upon a topic or issue that the reader can identify in his or her own life or experience.

Assignment: Write an essay in which you discuss the "truth" of the literature you have noted above. Support your point with evidence from your reading, classroom studies, and experience. Be sure to consider literature in all its forms, including songs, drama, film, television, and poetry.

Thesis: Write a *one-sentence* response to the above assignment. Make certain this single sentence offers a clear statement of your position.

> *Example: Because it shows the influence of world events on individuals, and depicts an authentic portrait of sacrificial love, Charles Dickens's* A Tale of Two Cities *reveals the truth about life, even though it is fiction.*

_____

_____

Organizational Plan: List at least three subtopics you will use to support your main idea. This list is your outline.

1. _____

2. _____

3. _____

Draft: Following your outline, write a good first draft of your essay. Remember to support all of your points with examples, facts, references to reading, etc.

Review and Revise: Exchange essays with a classmate. Using the scoring guide for Development on page 258, score your partner's essay (while he or she scores yours). Focus on the development of ideas and the use of language conventions. If necessary, rewrite your essay to incorporate more (or more relevant) support and/or improve your use of language.

Exercise VI

Improving Paragraphs

Read the following passage and then answer the multiple-choice questions that follow. The questions will require you to make decisions regarding the revision of the reading selection.

1   A book is now a common object, yet there was a time when the book was a rare and precious possession—a religious relic not available to the common person.

2   The earliest collections that we would recognize as "books" were elaborate manuscripts produced in European monasteries. To ensure that ancient knowledge would not be lost, monks made copies of the books they protected.

3   The books produced during this period were exquisitely and elaborately illuminated with beautiful lettering called calligraphy, and fantastic images of snakes, demons, and mythological creatures.

4   The most important thing about these manuscripts is that they were considered sacred objects. The monks who sat for years working on single chapters of the Bible were not reproducing books. They were making the word of God available to the world.

5   Eventually, the production of books moved from the Church to the University, and books began to lose some of their religious emphasis. University students did not have access to the books locked away in monasteries. Also, they needed access to new kinds of non-religious books that were not easily available even in the libraries of monasteries.

6   Two new kinds of institutions grew up around the universities to fulfill the demand: stationers and book copiers. These people provided paper and libraries of text books. When a student needed a text for a class, he would go to the stationers and copy it—by hand. The student could also pay a book copier to copy the book for him.

7   Then, the whole book-producing industry began to change with the arrival of the printing press. The printing press was not a single invention. It was born when printers **conflated** several technologies that had been known for centuries.

8   The other inventions brought together to create a printing press were the machines used for hundreds of years in Europe and Asia to press oil from olives and wine from grapes; block printing had been known in Europe since the return of Marco Polo from Asia.

9   The development of print technology created a need to develop new **tackle**. Medieval manuscripts had been copied on vellum pages—a material made largely from calfskin. It was beautiful and durable, but far too expensive for the mass production of books. Likewise, the ink that had been used by the monks and later by university students and book copiers was expensive. Oil-based ink needed to be developed as well as a paper that could be mass-produced inexpensively, yet still be durable enough to print a book that would last.

10   Ironically, the first books printed were Bibles and religious texts; so, while the printing press may have made books more available, it did not necessarily affect the subject matter of books.

11   However, by the 16th and 17th Centuries, the Roman Catholic Church was losing much of its influence. Latin had been the primary language for the worship of God and for the exchange of intellectual ideas, but this was changing with the Protestant Reformation. More people were learning to read, and they wanted to read things in their own language.

12   In addition, world exploration and the European colonization of Africa and the New World made people curious about faraway places. Writers and printers were only too happy to fill this demand for **copious** reading material for the curious middle classes. The modern book was born.

13   So the book on the shelf of a typical city library has a long and interesting ancestry that goes at least as far back as the monks in their medieval monasteries. Were it not for such different endeavors as wine-making and world travel, the book as we know it might never have been developed.

1. Which of the following revisions best clarifies the intent of paragraph 4?
   A. ...sacred objects because the monks...
   B. ...sacred objects, and the monks...
   C. ...sacred objects the monks...
   D. ...sacred objects, the monks...
   E. ...sacred objects; the monks...

2. Which of the following suggestions best corrects the awkward paragraph structure at the beginning of this selection?
   A. Add more material about the European monasteries.
   B. Delete paragraphs 2 and 3.
   C. Delete paragraphs 2 and 4.
   D. Combine paragraphs 2 and 3.
   E. Combine paragraphs 2 and 4.

3. What two paragraphs could be combined to make the passage easier to read?
   A. paragraphs 5 and 6
   B. paragraphs 7 and 8
   C. paragraphs 10 and 11
   D. paragraphs 10 and 12
   E. paragraphs 11 and 13

4. Which of the following revisions offers a better transition between paragraphs 6 and 7?
   A. Replace the first sentence of paragraph 7 with the sentence, "The tedium of hand-copying books was soon alleviated by the arrival of the printing press."
   B. "On the other hand, the whole book-producing industry began to change..."
   C. Replace *Then* in the first sentence of paragraph 7 with *However*.
   D. Use a semicolon to combine the last sentence of paragraph 6 with the first sentence of paragraph 7.
   E. Omit *Then*.

5. If the passage had to be shortened, what could be omitted without changing the intent of the passage?
   A. paragraphs 1 and 2
   B. paragraphs 5 and 6
   C. paragraphs 8 and 9
   D. paragraphs 10 and 11
   E. paragraphs 11 and 12

Review Lessons 1-3

Exercise I

Inferences

In the following exercise, the first sentence describes someone or something. Infer information from the first sentence, and then choose the word from the Word Bank that best completes the second sentence.

solvent	rote	dogmatic	ostracizes
conflates	restive	meticulous	proclivity

1. By looking very closely, one can see reflections of the imagined landscape in the lifelike eyes of the person in the painting.

    From this sentence, we can infer that the _____ artist included the finest of detail in the painting.

2. While other children were playing baseball or swimming, Ulysses was down by the river with a shovel all day, searching for unique rocks.

    From this sentence, we can infer that Ulysses has a[n] _____ for geology.

3. Ever since the traumatic circus accident at the park, Cory ducks and watches for stampeding elephants whenever he hears the bell of an ice cream truck.

    From this sentence, we can infer that Cory _____ the sound of ice cream trucks with threats to his life.

4. The professional pianist said that she does not consider herself ready for a concert until she has played the composition flawlessly 100 times in a row.

    From this sentence, we can infer that the pianist uses _____ methods to perfect her skills.

5. The police were sure the suspect had not told them everything about the incident because he never stopped sweating, stuttering, and squirming in his seat.

    From this sentence, we can infer that the police think the suspect's _____ behavior shows that he has something to hide.

Exercise II

Related Words

Some of the vocabulary words from Lessons 1 through 3 have related meanings. Complete the following sentences by choosing the word that best fits the context, based on information you infer from the use of the italicized word. Some word pairs will be antonyms, some will be synonyms, and some will simply be words often used in the same context.

1.   Though his father had committed the crime decades ago, the act was such *anathema*
      that the people of the town still _____ the father's descendants.
      A.   coerced
      B.   ostracized
      C.   divulged
      D.   castigated
      E.   occluded

2.   The bank manager unwittingly _____ the robbers when they noticed her
      furtive glance toward the notepad on which the vault combination had been written.
      A.   castigated
      B.   repined
      C.   abetted
      D.   ostracized
      E.   audited

3.   Because of her _____ opinion of the meat industry, Jen *conflates* all health
      problems in America with the consumption of meat.
      A.   gregarious
      B.   insipid
      C.   extraneous
      D.   docile
      E.   jaundiced

4.   Some students _____ to the theory that heavier objects fall faster than lighter
      objects, until Maury *disabused* them by demonstrating that a bowling ball and a
      penny fall at the same speed when dropped at the same moment.
      A.   divulged
      B.   ostracized
      C.   abetted
      D.   ascribed
      E.   coerced

5. Because their son had a[n] _____ for golf at an early age, the Winstons purchased all the *tackle* he needed to get out on the course and play.
   A. proclivity
   B. solvent
   C. avarice
   D. libation
   E. heresy

6. The _____ outlaw paced back and forth in his cell, knowing that the officials planned to *extradite* him back to the state in which he had committed his worst offenses.
   A. docile
   B. emaciated
   C. restive
   D. rote
   E. extraneous

7. The *emaciated* crash survivors used all their _____ to hike forty miles, with little food or water, across the frozen tundra to reach the village.
   A. proclivity
   B. disabuse
   C. anathema
   D. mettle
   E. mercenary

8. Considered *dogmatic* by even the strictest religious sects, the church considered it an act of _____ to even question the judgment of a high priest.
   A. libation
   B. heresy
   C. avarice
   D. ignominy
   E. bastion

9. The Bohemian section of the city hosted a *motley* convergence of ideas in art and literature, causing the area to become a[n] _____ of creativity and young talent.
   A. mercenary
   B. anathema
   C. avarice
   D. libation
   E. bastion

10. A[n] _____ of the town's financial records betrayed the treasurer's *avarice*; he had been writing checks to himself illegally for a few years.
    A. audit
    B. temerity
    C. proclivity
    D. libation
    E. solvent

Exercise III

Deeper Meanings

Choose a word to replace the italicized word in each sentence. All of the possible choices for each sentence have similar definitions, but the correct answer will have a connotation that best suits the context. For example, the words "delete," "destroy," and "obliterate" all mean "to remove or wipe out," but no one would ever say, "I destroyed the name from the document." The correct choice will be the word that has the best specific meaning and does not render the sentence awkward in tone or content. When choices seem close, look for a clue in the context that makes one choice better than the other.

Note that the correct answer is not always the primary vocabulary word from the lesson.

disabused	divulged	compliant	docile
dogmatic	experienced	administered	bossy
emaciated	attentive	informed	skinny
subservient	uncovered		

1. After forty years of success in the fried chicken business, Mr. Banks *told* his secret recipe to his grandchildren, so that they could take over the company.

   Better word: _____

2. The *strict* coach refused to try any plays that couldn't be found in the old playbook, even during losing seasons.

   Better word: _____

3. A line of customers stretching around the block quickly *enlightened* Damian of his belief that he had arrived early enough to buy concert tickets.

   Better word: _____

4. The *thin* patient suffered from the late stages of tuberculosis, in which the body cannot retain food or fluids.

   Better word: _____

5. The professor wanted his *submissive* students to learn how to think and not simply agree with everything he said.

   Better word: _____

Exercise IV

Crossword Puzzle

Use the clues to complete the crossword puzzle. The answers consist of vocabulary words from Lessons 1 through 3.

Across

1. provide the truth
4. gun for hire
7. ready to learn
10. help a criminal
12. gimme, gimme, gimme
14. sappy
15. give it up
16. like a perfectionist
17. on edge
18. throw overboard

Down

2. fortress
3. chew out
5. blame
6. daredevil fuel
8. refreshment
9. one too many
11. send back to the scene of the crime
13. plenty

Exercise V

Subject Prompts

Here is a writing prompt similar to the one you will find on the writing portion of an assessment test. Follow the instructions below and write a brief, efficient essay.

Imagine routinely diving for cover beneath your desk as practice for surviving a nuclear bomb. This was a reality for students in the United States and the Soviet Union during the height of the Cold War, prior to the fall of the Berlin Wall in 1989 and the subsequent collapse of the Soviet Union.

History attributes fifty years of peace to the Cold War: Two superpowers having the ability to annihilate each other prevented either side from starting a war. Many historians, therefore, ascribe to the maxim that applies to smaller segments of "an armed society is a polite society."

Based on your knowledge and belief of human nature, is the Cold War scenario a truism that applies to all people and all civilization? Will one nation, or person, naturally attempt to conquer the other simply because it has the means to conquer and cannot be stopped?

Base your argument on a situation in your own life, an example from world history, or an imagined scenario that resembles the situation of the Cold War, wherein the only thing preventing two people, or nations, from attacking one another is the fact that one would destroy the other in kind.

Thesis: Write a *one-sentence* response to the above assignment. Make certain this single sentence offers a clear statement of your position.

Example: If there is one constant in the history of humanity, it is that the stronger nation will influence, invade, or conquer the weaker nation.

_____

_____

Organizational Plan: List at least three subtopics you will use to support your main idea. This list is your outline.

1. _____

2. _____

3. _____

Draft: Following your outline, write a good first draft of your essay. Remember to support all your points with examples, facts, references to reading, etc.

Review and Revise: Exchange essays with a classmate. Using the scoring guide for Organization on page 257, score your partner's essay (while he or she scores yours). Focus on the organizational plan and the use of language conventions. If necessary, rewrite your essay to improve the organizational plan and/or your use of language.

Lesson Four

1. **despondent** (də spon´ dənt) *adj.* feeling gloomy or hopeless
Knowing that his error had cost the team its undefeated status, the *despondent* player sat in the corner of the dugout and stared at the floor.
syn: dejected; dismal   *ant: joyful; buoyant*

2. **protocol** (prō´ tə kəl) *n.* the formal or official way of correctly doing something
The pilot adhered to the proper *protocol* for an engine failure and was able to safely land the jet.
syn: custom; code

3. **candid** (kan´ did) *adj.* honest and straightforward; blunt
He gave a *candid* speech about the time he had spent in prison.
syn: frank; direct   *ant: evasive*

4. **jingoism** (jing´ gō iz əm) *n.* extreme, chauvinistic patriotism, often favoring an aggressive, warlike foreign policy
Because of his *jingoism*, the candidate lost the support of voters.

5. **redress** (rē dres´) *v.* to make right; to correct
The teacher *redressed* his earlier statement about Genghis Khan after he realized his error.
syn: rectify; amend   *ant: exacerbate; worsen*

6. **argot** (är´ gət) *n.* special words or phrases used by a specific group of people
Don't agree to "a trip to the East River" proposed by anyone speaking Mafia *argot*.
syn: jargon

7. **appease** (ə pēz´) *v.* to calm; to make satisfied (often only temporarily)
The small snack before dinner did nothing to *appease* Shane's appetite.
syn: mollify   *ant: aggravate*

8. **strident** (strīd´ nt) *adj.* harsh sounding; grating
Lisa's *strident* voice gave us all headaches.
syn: shrill   *ant: soothing*

9. **chaos** (kā´ os) *n.* complete disorder
The new teacher was expected to end the *chaos* and restore order in the classroom.
syn: confusion; jumble   *ant: order; harmony*

10. **expunge** (ik spunj´) *v.* to erase or eliminate
If Moni can stay out of trouble for one year, her criminal record will be *expunged*.
syn: obliterate   *ant: add*

11. **bigot** (big´ ət)   *n.*   one who is intolerant of differences in others
    The *bigot* refused to share a cab with anyone of a different race.
    syn: racist; extremist

12. **augment** (ôg ment´)   *v.*   to enlarge; to increase in amount or intensity
    I had to take a second job to *augment* my income after buying the new SUV.
    syn: expand; supplement   *ant: narrow; reduce*

13. **toilsome** (toi´ əl sum)   *adj.*   requiring exhaustive effort; laborious
    Of all the household chores, the *toilsome* task of pulling weeds out of the flower
    garden was Eleanor's least favorite.
    syn: grueling; arduous   *ant: easy; effortless*

14. **negligence** (neg´ li jəns)   *n.*   careless neglect, often resulting in injury
    Sara's *negligence* allowed her toddler to fall from the hotel balcony.
    syn: carelessness   *ant: care; attention*

15. **privation** (prī vā´ shun)   *n.*   lack of basic life necessities; extreme poverty
    Because Luke had experienced *privation* as a child, he appreciated many things in
    life that most people took for granted.
    syn: impoverishment; penury   *ant: wealth; luxury*

Exercise I

Words in Context

From the list below, supply the words needed to complete the paragraph. Some words will not be used.

augment	jingoism	argot	candid
chaos	appease		

1. The Prime Minister faced a tough decision in order to _argot_ an angered nation. The _jingoism_ resulting from the surprise attack fueled widespread _appease_, and citizens were tired of the administration's inaction. When he finally spoke, the Prime Minister delivered a[n] _candid_ address that revealed both his anger and his plan of counterattack.

From the list below, supply the words needed to complete the paragraph. Some words will not be used.

negligence	augment	expunge	bigot
argot	strident	chaos	tradition

2. The ridiculous arguments of the outspoken _chaos_ became too much for his opponents in the general population. When the man began to use the _bigot_ of the despised slave trade to encourage his followers and _strident_ his arguments, many college-age protesters began to attend his rallies. Their _negligence_ voices condemned not only the speaker, but also the _augment_ of the government in allowing his presence at state-funded institutions. The majority of students wished that his views could be _expunge_ from society.

From the list below, supply the words needed to complete the paragraph. Some words will not be used.

argot	despondent	augment	privation
toilsome	protocol	redress	

3. Vedant endured _toilsom_ as a child living in the slums of Mumbai, making pennies a day through the _privatio_ job of sorting through bits of recyclable trash. Losing his mother and older brother to disease had left Vedant _redress_ even among his friends, because his losses left him feeling that the proper _despondent_ for survival would be to avoid getting close to anyone, lest they go away like his family. Fortunately, Vedant was able to escape his poverty as a teenager and later, as a married man of modest success, look back and _augment_ his dire philosophy of life, having learned to seek the comforts of friendship.

Exercise II

Sentence Completion

Complete the sentence in a way that shows you understand the meaning of the italicized vocabulary word.

1. Ryan has been *despondent* ever since... His Dad died

2. My math teacher said he would *expunge* the "F" from my record if I... did extra credit

3. The people forced to live in *privation* rarely... eat

4. When I babysat the Patelli twins, my *negligence* led to... one dead

5. I thought it was fair to accuse George of *jingoism* after he... Hit that woman

6. The atmosphere on the commuter train became one of *chaos* when... That guy got killed

7. Toby hates the *toilsome* job of... cleaning

8. The *argot* of pirates might include terms such as... yo ho

9. I realized my grandfather was a *bigot* when he told me... He hates black people

10. One way to *appease* a crying child is... Feeding them

11. My brother's voice becomes *strident* when he... plays golf

12. If I wanted to *augment* my savings account, I might... get a job

13. If you think your house is on fire, the best *protocol* is... Stop drop and roll

14. Theresa was *candid* about my new haircut; she told me that... It looked weird

15. The mayor attempted to *redress* the horrible situation in the city by... Saying everything was fine

Exercise III

Roots, Prefixes, and Suffixes

Study the entries and answer the questions that follow.

The root *alter* means "change" or "other."
The root *ego* means "self."
The root *mega* means "large."
The root *polis* means "city" or "state."
The root *centris* means "centered on."

1. Using *literal* translations as guidance, define the following words without using a dictionary:

   A. megalopolis D. metropolitan
   B. alteration   E. egotist
   C. alter ego   F. egocentric

2. A person who is a *megalomaniac* might not feel right unless
   _____.

3. If you *alter* your plans, you _____.

4. List as many words as you can think of that begin with the root *ego*, and then do the same for the root *mega*.

Exercise IV

Inference

Complete the sentence by inferring information about the italicized word from its context.

1. If Colleen made *strident* sounds while practicing her saxophone, her parents probably... don't practice at home

2. The writer took offense at Marty's *candid* review because it... Potrayed him completly wrong

3. When *negligence* becomes the main reason for damaged goods and low profits, the plant managers will probably... get in trouble

Exercise V

Critical Reading

Below is a pair of reading passages followed by several multiple-choice questions. Carefully read the passages and choose the best answer for each of the questions.

Passage 1

The Commonwealth of Pennsylvania is a wealth of natural resources, and the bounty has been claimed and reclaimed. The vast native forests and rich coal deposits built countless railroads and boroughs dotting the valleys of the Keystone State. There has been a price for the commodities. Timbering wiped out Pennsylvania hardwood forests when loggers clamored for the mas-
5 sive white pines—the preferred lumber a century ago. Dozens of spent mines, years after their usefulness, leaked iron and sulfur into creeks, making the water uninhabitable to native trout for decades. Whitetail deer were hunted to virtual extinction by 1900. Nature is slow to recover, but after dozens of years, extensive legislation, and millions of dollars in reclamation funds, the forests have since grown back, and streams and forests teem with trout and deer. Now the allure
10 of natural gas has again forced many residents to weigh the risks of extracting the prize from the earth. Every prize comes with risk, and sometimes the risk is that of losing the treasure itself. Consider the lessons learned in the mining town of Centralia.

All the small towns in the coal-rich hills of Central Pennsylvania look pretty much alike, except for Centralia. With a population of 10, Centralia is a 21st-century ghost town. In the early 1960s,
15 Centralia was a prosperous little town of 1,100 residents. People were friendly, and neighbors watched out for one another; however, all that changed in 1962 when the town selected an exhausted strip mine just outside of town as the site of a new landfill. In May of that year, a fire broke out at the dump and proved to be too **toilsome** to extinguish. Not long after the landfill fire, it was discovered that a seam of coal beneath the landfill—a seam of coal that ran in an intricate
20 web beneath the town itself—had caught fire.

That was over 50 years ago, and the fire still burns today. Sulfurous smoke vents through cracks in the pavement. Houses have collapsed into sink holes caused by mine subsidence, and the number of residents has dwindled from 1,100 to virtually none.

In 1984, after repeated and expensive attempts by state and federal agencies to extinguish or
25 contain the fire, the federal government finally allocated $42 million to **appease** residents by purchasing their homes and businesses, which allowed them to relocate. Since then, efforts have continued to remove residents from harm and close this sad story of human error and inevitable consequences.

Passage 2

On April 1, 1996—April Fools' Day—the United States Supreme Court denied an appeal of the few remaining residents of Centralia, Pennsylvania, who had filed preliminary legal objections to the condemnation of their homes. With this denial, these hapless citizens essentially lost the right to their homes. Residents who chose to stay beyond the December 31, 1997, relocation deadline
5 would forfeit the right to compensation from any federal or state agency or any private enterprise for losses suffered, including loss of life.

The issue at hand was a 34-year-old mine fire burning beneath the homes, businesses, and streets of Centralia. What seemed to be an unfortunate accident in May of 1962 is now considered by some to have been a conspiracy on the part of the United States government to seize the rich
10   coal deposits that lie beneath the town and surrounding areas.

Proponents of the conspiracy theory cite a list of facts to substantiate it. Supposedly, holes in the strip mine that allowed the fire to travel beneath the surface had been sealed before the site was approved for use as a landfill. The Pennsylvania government inspected and certified the site as safe to use; however, a few days after the 1962 fire, firefighters found a hole that had been left
15   open through supposed **negligence**. In addition, the Department of Natural Resources drilled boreholes to monitor the underground fire—boreholes that subsequently **augmented** the fire by providing more oxygen, which allowed it to spread.

What seemed to be half-hearted attempts to extinguish the fire fostered further suspicion from conspiracy theorists. Only one serious attempt to control the burn occurred in 1968 over a holi-
20   day weekend. Firefighters dug a trench to halt the spread of the fire; however, crews worked only one daily shift, rather than the 24-hour shifts necessary to contain the fire. Crews even stopped for the holiday; by the time they returned, the fire had spread beyond the trench. Neither did the federal government try to **redress** the situation other than in purchasing the homes in Centralia and relocating the residents. The Commonwealth of Pennsylvania condemned the properties of
25   the remaining residents in 1992, but failed to help bring legal action to protect the rights and homes of the former Centralia residents. In 1996, the Supreme Court denied any possibility of legal action on the part of the residents and the Commonwealth of Pennsylvania.

A compromise reached in 2013 allowed the few remaining residents to live out their lives in Centralia, but they suspect that when the last person leaves, the government will seize the land
30   through eminent domain, miraculously discover the means to extinguish the fire, and mine the millions of dollars in coal beneath the ground.

Is Centralia's plight the product of a government conspiracy or is it simply a tragic accident? Perhaps the future will bring answers, but for those whose entire family histories have been lost, it's been a sad story that hasn't yet ended.

1A.   The effect of the introductory paragraph in passage 1, is best described as an attempt to
    A.   show Centralia as an especially unique situation for any place in the world.
    B.   suggest the importance of clean water for native fish, tree growth, and mine recovery.
    C.   attack corporations that exploit natural resources without paying enough taxes.
    D.   portray Centralia as just one of many examples of the risks of using natural resources.
    E.   establish the time period and historical context in which the Centralia incident occurred.

1B.   What idea does the author of passage 1 hope to establish in lines 14-17?
    A.   Life was hard in Centralia, Pennsylvania, even before the fire.
    B.   Prior to the fire, Centralia, Pennsylvania, was a thriving metropolis.
    C.   The early 1960s were a period of vast change for the United States.
    D.   Centralia, Pennsylvania, was a typical small town before the fire.
    E.   Centralia, Pennsylvania, was an inappropriate place for a landfill.

2A. The overall tone of the first passage can best be described as
    A.   sympathetic.
    B.   apathetic.
    C.   ironic.
    D.   condemning.
    E.   hostile.

2B. Which phrase from passage 1 best supports your answer to question 2A?
    A.   "sad story of human error"
    B.   "all that changed in 1962"
    C.   "21st-century ghost town"
    D.   "Nature is slow to recover"
    E.   "Every prize comes with risk"

3.   As used in passage 1, line 22, the word *subsidence* most nearly means
    A.   payments.
    B.   relocation.
    C.   condemning.
    D.   replenishment.
    E.   erosion.

4A. The author of passage 1 ascribes the blame for the Centralia fire to
    A.   former residents of Centralia.
    B.   the state government.
    C.   the mayor.
    D.   the federal government.
    E.   no group in particular.

4B. Choose the phrase from passage 1 that best supports your answer to question 4A.
    A.   "the number of residents has dwindled"
    B.   "story of human error and inevitable consequences"
    C.   "efforts have continued to remove residents from harm"
    D.   "the allure of natural gas"
    E.   "a seam of coal beneath the landfill…had caught fire"

4C. The phrase "repeated and expensive attempts" (line 24, passage 1) implies
    A.   everything possible was done to extinguish or contain the fire.
    B.   the fire had cost the residents a great deal of money.
    C.   the government avoided the costs of containing the fire.
    D.   new advances in firefighting technology make a solution imminently probable.
    E.   the cost of extinguishing the fire exceeded the cost of replacing homes.

5A. The overall tone of the second passage can best be described as
    A.   bitterly ironic.
    B.   thoroughly condemning.
    C.   blandly objective.
    D.   mildly reproachful.
    E.   severely critical.

5B. How does the content of lines 11-31, passage 2, support your choice for the answer
to question 5A?
A.   It emphasizes the town's negligence in stopping the fire.
B.   It balances positive and negative criticism of the government.
C.   It portrays the federal government as having reacted immediately.
D.   It demands restitution for the residents of Centralia.
E.   It contains a list of government failures.

5C. The best substitute for the word *substantiate*, as it is used in line 11, passage 2, is
A.   drop.
B.   attempt.
C.   confirm.
D.   disprove.
E.   increase.

6A. The probable intent of the reference to April Fools' Day in the first sentence of
passage 2 is to
A.   establish the exact date of the Supreme Court's decision.
B.   emphasize the perseverance of the residents of Centralia.
C.   imply that the Supreme Court's decision was foolish.
D.   highlight the irony that the Supreme Court's decision was handed down in
spring.
E.   reinforce the importance of the issue to the residents of Centralia.

6B. Which phrase from passage 2, paragraph 1, reveals sentiment toward the residents of
Centralia?
A.   "private enterprise"
B.   "hapless citizens"
C.   "legal objections"
D.   "condemnation of their homes"
E.   "loss of life"

7A. In passage 2, which of the following is not a factor in the suspected conspiracy?
A.   The Commonwealth of Pennsylvania inspected the strip mine and certified it
for use as a landfill.
B.   Boreholes drilled by the Department of Natural Resources may have provided
oxygen and allowed the fire to spread.
C.   Crews worked too slowly on the containment ditch.
D.   Residents of Centralia have been denied legal appeals to the condemnation of
their homes.
E.   The Supreme Court denial was handed down on April Fools' Day.

7B. How would the meaning of the line, "Crews even stopped for the holiday; by the time they returned, the fire had spread beyond the trench" (lines 21-22, passage 2), change, if the word *even* were deleted?
   A. It would be less critical of the crews.
   B. It would remain the same.
   C. It would be more skeptical of the crews.
   D. It would change the object of the author's comment to the residents.
   E. It would create a less positive portrayal of the crews.

8. What does the author of passage 2 conclude about the likelihood that the Centralia mine fire is a government conspiracy?
   A. The author comes to no absolute conclusion, citing only what residents claim.
   B. The author sums up the facts of the case and suggests that a conspiracy is possible.
   C. The author sums up the facts of the case and suggests that a conspiracy is not likely.
   D. The author clearly and succinctly demonstrates the unlikelihood of a conspiracy.
   E. The author offers no conclusion, but expresses sympathy for the residents.

9A. The authors of both passages would probably disagree over which one of the following statements?
   A. Centralia was just one of many similar, recurring, ecological accidents.
   B. The Centralia fire created many hardships for the residents of the town.
   C. The world must weigh the risks of obtaining natural resources.
   D. Coal is valuable fuel, but mines can be dangerous.
   E. The federal government can take many years to resolve incidents.

9B. Choose the most appropriate title for passage 2.
   A. The History of Centralia
   B. The Centralia Accident and Its Causes
   C. Who Really Burned Centralia?
   D. The Possibilities of Secret Deals for Coal
   E. When Mines Burn

10A. If passage 1 were to appear as an article in a school textbook, which subject would that textbook probably be?
   A. business
   B. literature
   C. mathematics
   D. chemistry
   E. history

10B. Passage 2 could be said to be advocating for which group of people?
   A. the residents who left Centralia
   B. the local government
   C. the last remaining residents of Centralia
   D. the federal government
   E. people who wish to build new homes in Centralia

Lesson Five

1. **retinue** (re´ ti nōō) *n.* followers or servants who accompany an important person
The prince's *retinue* quickly abandoned him when he was discovered to be an impostor.
syn: entourage; cortege

2. **disparity** (di spar´ i tē) *n.* inequality; difference
My wife is twelve years older than I am, but we get along well despite the *disparity* in our ages.
syn: gap   *ant: similarity*

3. **extol** (ik stōl´) *v.* to praise highly
Emily *extolled* the virtues of her personal hero and mentor.
syn: exalt; laud   *ant: chastise*

4. **conscript** (kon skript´) *v.* to force someone into military service
As defeat loomed over the dictator's troops, he *conscripted* women, children, and old men to fight against the invading army.

5. **rancor** (rang´ kər) *n.* extreme hatred or ill will
Whelan's double-dealing had Jack seething; he had never before felt so much *rancor* toward a lawyer.
syn: animosity; enmity   *ant: amity; sympathy*

6. **clement** (klem´ ənt) *adj.* merciful; lenient
Despite the abhorrent nature of the crime, the judge handed down a surprisingly *clement* sentence.
syn: forbearing; benign   *ant: malevolent; harsh*

7. **unfettered** (un fe´ tûrd) *adj.* free from restrictions
The knights chose to engage in combat *unfettered* by their bulky steel helmets.
syn: free; unrestrained   *ant: restricted*

8. **adamant** (ad´ ə mant) *adj.* unyielding; firm in opinion
Despite the protests of the entire city council, the mayor remained *adamant*.
syn: stubborn   *ant: amenable; flexible*

9. **impute** (im pūt´) *v.* to credit with cause or fault
Experts *imputed* the team's loss to an inexperienced coach.
syn: attribute; ascribe

10. **diffident**   (dif´ i dənt)   *adj.*   lacking in self-confidence; shy
    The *diffident* student hated to speak in front of the class.
    syn: timid   *ant: outgoing*

11. **ostensible**   (o sten´ sə bəl)   *adj.*   professed but not necessarily true
    The *ostensible* reason for inviting her up to his room was to show her his bottle cap
    collection.
    syn: supposed   *ant: actual*

12. **inexorable**   (in ek´ sər ə bal)   *adj.*   unrelenting; unavoidable
    Decades of harsh weather caused the *inexorable* erosion of the tombstone.
    syn: relentless; certain   *ant: avoidable; preventable*

13. **cliché**   (klē shā´)   *n.*   a worn-out idea or overused expression
    The candidate promised new ideas, but spouted only old *clichés* about government
    after her election.
    syn: platitude; banality

14. **opus**   (ō´ pəs)   *n.*   a creative work, especially a numbered composition (The plural
    of *opus* is *opera*.)
    My favorite composition by Antonín Dvořák is *Opus* 95.

15. **prate**   (prāt)   *v.*   to talk pointlessly and at length
    During the flight from Houston to Honolulu, Dan listened to two people *prate* about
    a terrible TV reality show for eight straight hours.
    syn: prattle; yak

Exercise I

Words in Context

From the list below, supply the words needed to complete the paragraph. Some words will not be used.

rancor   extol   adamant   cliché
ostensible   clement   disparity

1. I wish that I could _____ your recent work, but as the _____ goes, workers like you are a dime a dozen. I've been keeping you on the payroll despite your recent incompetence, but it must end now. The president is _____ about cutting unnecessary costs, so I'm afraid that I'm going to have to let you go. I can't be _____ with you any longer.

From the list below, supply the words needed to complete the paragraph. Some words will not be used.

inexorable   disparity   opus   diffident
ostensible   clement   rancor

2. When the manager noticed the _____ between the amount of cash in the register and the total of the nightly bank deposit, he never suspected Yvonne. Although _____ and mild mannered in the office, she would engage in arguments filled with _____ and threats at home; her husband knew that the _____ result of her stealing would be jail. She felt, however, that one huge theft of the company payroll would be construed as the work of an outsider, not the grand, climactic _____ of her career in crime.

From the list below, supply the words needed to complete the paragraph. Some words will not be used.

retinue   cliché   conscript   impute
prate   unfettered   extol

3. There were few volunteers among Captain Hawley's crew of privateers; the captain _____ most of them, giving them the choice of sinking with their plundered ships or joining his crew. England _____ Hawley in at least ten acts of piracy, but never captured him. Like most privateers, Hawley was _____ of the traditional maritime laws and could thus choose his targets freely. Traitors among Hawley's crew often _____ secretly about mutiny, but it would have been almost impossible to fight past the captain's personal _____ of trusted officers.

Exercise II

Sentence Completion

Complete the sentence in a way that shows you understand the meaning of the italicized vocabulary word.

1. The queen had to *conscript* sailors because…

2. The *cliché*, "to tie the knot," actually means…

3. The advance of the invading forces seemed *inexorable* until…

4. Aunt Rita's *adamant* belief in superstition causes her to…

5. The Air Force *imputed* a flock of Canada geese for…

6. Carol's *ostensible* purpose was charity, but she really wanted…

7. If the security guards sit around and *prate*, then they might…

8. The *disparity* among our political opinions sometimes results in…

9. Devon's *rancor* over excessive violence on TV made him…

10. The movie star's *retinue* included…

11. The *clement* weather will…

12. A *diffident* person will probably never become…

13. The Speedy-Mart manager *extolled* Jeremy for…

14. The composer's latest *opus* will be played by…

15. When manufacturing is *unfettered* by rules on safety,…

Exercise III

Roots, Prefixes, and Suffixes

Study the entries and answer the questions that follow.

The prefix *circum*– means "around, on all sides."
The root *naviga* means "to sail, to steer."
The prefixes *intro*– and *intra*– mean "in, within, inside of."
The roots *spec* and *spect* mean "to see, look at."
The roots *vert* and *vers* mean "to turn."
The root *locu* means "speaking."
The prefix *extro*– means "outside."

1. Using *literal* translations as guidance, define the following words without using a dictionary:

    A. circumnavigate   D. introspect
    B. retrospect   E. circumlocutions
    C. introvert   F. extrovert

2. List as many words as you can think of that contain the root *spec* and the root *vert*. Try to define each word literally.

3. List as many words as you can think of that contain the prefix *circum*– and the prefix *intro*–. Try to define each word literally.

Exercise IV

Inference

Complete the sentence by inferring information about the italicized word from its context.

1. The judge was *clement* when she sentenced the offender, so the crime was probably…

2. Because Shelly is so *adamant* about not accepting birthday gifts, her friends could…

3. Sierra produced twice as many widgets as needed, so her supervisor *extolled* her by…

Exercise V

Writing

Here is a writing prompt similar to the one you will find on the writing portion of an assessment test.

Plan and write an essay based on the following statement:

> I'm always amazed that people will actually choose to sit in front of the television and just be savaged by stuff that belittles their intelligence.
>
> –Alice Walker

Assignment: Write an essay in which you interpret the above statement, and describe whether you agree or disagree. Be certain to support and illustrate your points with specific references to your experiences and observations, and consider television of all genres, including movies and series.

Thesis: Write a *one-sentence* response to the above assignment. Make certain this single sentence offers a clear statement of your position.

Example: Though Alice Walker may believe that everything on television insults human intelligence, I find many programs to be the best stories I have ever heard.

_____

_____

Organizational Plan: List at least three subtopics you will use to support your main idea. This list is your outline.

1. _____

2. _____

3. _____

Draft: Following your outline, write a good first draft of your essay. Remember to support all your points with examples, facts, references to reading, etc.

Review and Revise: Exchange essays with a classmate. Using the scoring guide for Sentence Formation and Variety on page 260, score your partner's essay (while he or she scores yours). Focus on sentence structure and the use of language conventions. If necessary, rewrite your essay to improve the sentence structure and/or your use of language.

Exercise VI

English Practice

Identifying Sentence Errors

Identify the grammatical error in each of the following sentences. If the sentence contains no error, select answer choice E.

1. <u>Many people</u> go to the movies <u>to escape reality</u>, but <u>my best friend and me</u>
       (A)   (B)   (C)
    go <u>to be entertained</u>.   <u>No error</u>
          (D)   (E)

2. Everyone <u>should have</u> a dream that <u>they can</u> strive for, <u>even if</u> it sometimes
             (A)   (B)   (C)
    <u>seems</u> impossible to achieve.   <u>No error</u>
     (D)   (E)

3. <u>If</u> Deanna or Katie <u>win</u> the election <u>for class president,</u> <u>I'll be disappointed</u>.
    (A)   (B)   (C)   (D)
    <u>No error</u>
     (E)

4. <u>I laughed</u> when I saw <u>my neighbor, Mr. Bean,</u> <u>yelling at people in the street</u>
       (A)   (B)   (C)
    <u>in his long underwear</u>.   <u>No error</u>
        (D)   (E)

5. <u>During the holidays,</u> <u>my family</u> and I <u>traveled further</u> than <u>we did</u> last year.
        (A)   (B)   (C)   (D)
    <u>No error</u>
     (E)

Improving Sentences

The underlined portion of each sentence below contains some flaw. Select the answer choice that best corrects the flaw.

6. Because I relied on my calculator so often, <u>I had forgotten how to do long division.</u>
    A. I forgot how to do long division.
    B. I have forgotten how long division works.
    C. I forget how to do long division.
    D. long division had become impossible.
    E. long division became a mystery.

7. My parents trusted me with their new car because I passed the driving test without a problem, I studied for it for more than a month.
   A. My parents trusted me with their new car because I passed the driving test without a problem, but I spent more than a month studying for it.
   B. My parents trusted me with their new car because I passed the driving test without a problem, and I studied for it for more than a month.
   C. My parents trusted me with their new car because I passed the driving test without a problem, even though I had studied for it for more than a month.
   D. My parents, who trusted me with their new car because I passed the driving test without a problem, and studied for it for more than a month.
   E. My parents trusted me with their new car, because I passed the driving test without a problem, yet studied for it for more than a month.

8. In the United States, we can vote and will be able to sign contracts legally at the age of 18.
   A. we can vote and then sign contracts…
   B. we vote and can sign contracts…
   C. we can vote and sign contracts…
   D. we can vote and are permitted to sign contracts…
   E. we can vote and are able to sign contracts…

9. Do the people who use cell phones driving cause more accidents than are caused by others?
   A. Do the people on cell phones while driving cause more accidents than are caused by others?
   B. Do the people who use cell phones while they are driving cause more accidents than other people will do?
   C. Do the people who use cell phones driving cause more accidents than others?
   D. Do the people who use cell phones while driving cause more accidents than people who don't use them?
   E. Do the people who use cell phones driving cause more accidents than those who don't use cell phones while driving?

10. Natalie raised her voice above the loud music to be heard.
    A. above the loud music, so people would be able to hear her.
    B. to be heard above the loud music.
    C. above the loud music so her words could be heard.
    D. over the noise to be heard.
    E. so that she would be able to be clearly heard over the very loud music.

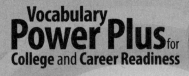

Vocabulary
Power Plus for
College and Career Readiness

LEVEL

Lesson Six

1. **credence** (krēd´ ns) *n.* belief or trust
Surprisingly, Shayna's teacher gave *credence* to her story about how she lost her homework.
syn: faith; confidence   *ant: disbelief*

2. **collate** (kō´ lāt) *v.* to arrange into the proper order, especially documents
Before he began his delivery route, the mailman *collated* his deliveries to match the order of the streets he would visit.
syn: organize; assemble

3. **connoisseur** (kon ə sûr´) *n.* an expert in matters of culture, food, or wine
The chef watched nervously as the *connoisseur* tasted the soup.
                                        ant: tyro; novice; neophyte

4. **enigma** (i nig´ mə) *n.* a mystery; something seemingly inexplicable
Mona Lisa's smile is an *enigma* because no one knows the thoughts behind her inscrutable expression.
syn: riddle; puzzle

5. **genteel** (jen tēl´) *adj.* polite and respectable in manner
A *genteel* host would never ask guests to prepare and serve their own dinner.
syn: refined; cultured   *ant: boorish; rude*

6. **officious** (ə fish´ əs) *adj.* excessively eager to deliver unasked for or unwanted help
I wish my *officious* sister would stop telling me how to run my life.
syn: meddlesome; interfering

7. **fetid** (fe´ təd) *adj.* having a bad odor
The gym teacher told students to remove the *fetid* heaps of dirty clothes from their lockers and take the mess home.
syn: rank; reeking   *ant: fragrant; aromatic*

8. **jaunty** (jôn´ tē) *adj.* having a buoyant, self-confident air; brisk and crisp
My three-year-old always walks in a *jaunty* manner when I put him in that sailor suit.
syn: confident; poised

9. **condone** (kən dōn´) *v.* to forgive or overlook an offense
After hearing about the man's starving family, most found it easy to *condone* his theft of the food.
syn: pardon; excuse   *ant: condemn*

10. **torpor** (tôr´ pər) *n.*   a state of sluggish mental or physical activity; a state of not caring
    The *torpor* of the audience was evidence of the comedian's lack of talent.
    syn: apathy; indifference   *ant: interest; eagerness*

11. **enthrall** (en thral´) *v.* to captivate as though spellbound
    The television *enthralled* the villagers, who had never before seen such technology.
    syn: charm; enchant   *ant: repulse*

12. **dilettante** (dil i tänt´) *n.*   one who merely dabbles in an art or a science
    The *dilettante* felt that his superficial knowledge of art qualified him to judge the artist's work.
    syn: amateur; trifler   *ant: expert; professional*

13. **venal** (vē´ nəl) *adj.*   capable of betraying trust, especially if bribed
    During the war, the queen worried about having *venal* subjects who would betray her for a high-enough reward.
    syn: corrupt; crooked   *ant: upright; honest*

14. **nuance** (nōō´ äns) *n.*   a slight or subtle degree of difference
    The sharpest listeners detected a *nuance* in the speaker's tone that revealed her opinion.
    syn: gradation; shade

15. **cult** (kult) *n.*   an organized group of people with an obsessive devotion to a person or set of principles
    To join the *cult*, recruits had to shave their heads and walk over burning coals.
    syn: sect

Exercise I

Words in Context

From the list below, supply the words needed to complete the paragraph. Some words will not be used.

condone   nuance   connoisseur   torpor
officious   cult   credence   dilettante

1.   The chef, tucked away in the kitchen, nervously awaited the report from the latest critic. Knowing that Mr. Tahoma was a[n] _Connoisseur_ of Peruvian cuisine and a weekly newspaper columnist with a[n] _cult_ following, the chef hoped that the waiters refrained from the _torpor_ behavior that well-known food critics must often endure from servers. The chef had run the restaurant for twenty-eight years; he was certainly not a[n] _dilettante_ in matters of cooking, but owing to a decline in customers, he worried about the fate of the business. He could only hope that Mr. Tahoma would rave about the many subtle _nuances_ in the meal. A positive review, combined with the _credence_ accorded to the column, might be all that the chef needed to save the restaurant.

From the list below, supply the words needed to complete the paragraph. Some words will not be used.

credence   condone   nuance   enigma
torpor   jaunty

2.   Though she was a hostess at the restaurant, Rolinda remained seated, even as customers entered the waiting area. Revealing her _____ over hungry suburbanites, Rolinda confined herself to a sigh and let younger servers greet the new potential tippers at the door. She knew that her manager would not _____ her behavior so she took her place in front of the main table. Rolinda also wondered why, even though she hadn't been sick, she had been so tired for the last month. If she didn't solve this _____ soon, she would more than likely lose her job. For another day, she would just have to put on a fake smile and affect a[n] _____ manner until the end of her shift.

From the list below, supply the words needed to complete the paragraph. Some words will not be used.

fetid   torpor   genteel   officious
venal   collate   enthrall

3.   The sight of the city skyline in the distance _____ Eddie, who had never been to the foreign metropolis, but the _____ smell emanating from mounds of trash surrounding the suburban apartment buildings quickly made him wonder if the city were as _____ as the movies had often portrayed it. He would learn over the next few weeks that the only way to conduct business was to bribe the legion of _____ city clerks to process paperwork or else it would simply be "lost" behind a filing cabinet, or the clerks would _____ the stacks so that applicants who didn't bribe would be placed on the bottom of the pile.

Exercise II

Sentence Completion

Complete the sentence in a way that shows you understand the meaning of the italicized vocabulary word.

1. The *fetid* smell was coming from… The Onion

2. The magician *enthralled* everyone when… He did trick

3. Nick had a *jaunty* walk after… He found out his dad did died

4. To show their loyalty, members of the *cult* wear… bed Sheets

5. The *dilettante* never grew tired of watching the stars, hoping someday to… be on the moon

6. The rare cadillac was at the top of the *connoisseur's* want list, so she… got one

7. There was only a slight *nuance* of difference between… them

8. Giving *credence* to the refugees' story, the border guard… Arrested them for immigration

9. Kenton suffered from the *torpor* brought on by… School

10. "This case is quite an *enigma*," said the detective. "We'll be lucky to… Solve it

11. Parents cannot *condone* their children's actions when… they do drugs

12. After enduring her *officious* mother for more than thirty years, Loren decided to… Kill her

13. The *genteel* society could not understand why… old yeller died

14. A single, *venal* night watchman was to blame for… the Heist

15. Please *collate* your term paper before… your right

Exercise III

Roots, Prefixes, and Suffixes

Study the entries and answer the questions that follow.

The root *arch* means "to be first," "rule," or "govern."
The roots *dem* and *demos* mean "people."
The roots *mit* and *mis* mean "send."
The suffix *–ist* means "one who practices or believes."
The suffix *–cracy* means "rule by."
The suffix *–graphy* means "writing about" or "study of."

1. Using *literal* translations as guidance, define the following words without using a dictionary:

    A. archetype   D. demography
    B. transmit   E. monarchy
    C. democracy   F. remit

2. A *technocrat* would be a supporter of _____.

3. The root *oligos* means "few"; therefore, an *oligarchy* would probably be

    _____.

4. List as many words as you can think of that contain the forms *arch, dem, mit, mis,* or *crat.*

5. The prefix *an–* means "without" or "against." An *anarchist* is

    _____.

Exercise IV

Inference

Complete the sentence by inferring information about the italicized word from its context.

1. When the *torpor* of your coworkers causes them to miss deadlines, the best way to get them motivated is to… *Cat*

2. The *connoisseur* refused a considerable sum to endorse the fast-food chain because she believed that… *Cat*

3. The cause of the dog's odd behavior remains an *enigma,* so the owner will probably… *Cat*

Exercise V

Critical Reading

Below is a reading passage followed by several multiple-choice questions. Carefully read the passage and choose the best answer for each of the questions.

Over three hundred years ago, Alexander Pope wrote, in an essay, "A little learning is a danger-ous thing." Pope's statement is a truth for every time and place, even among the most learned people in civilization.

Little Boy and Fat Man, the only two atomic bombs to be used offensively in the history of the
5   world, ended the war with Japan in 1945 and thrust the world into the atomic age. The awesome and terrible power of these first fission bombs was the product of the most massive secret project in all of warfare: the Manhattan Project. The project involved more than 120,000 people, includ-ing some of the brightest scientists of the century—mathematicians and nuclear physicists from several nations.

10   Nuclear weapons and energy research became the top priority after the end of the war, and the veteran scientists of the Manhattan Project passed on knowledge to the next generation of nuclear scientists. Like members of a secret, atomic **cult**, the geniuses set about solving the **enigma** of harnessing atomic power. In spite of cutting-edge advancements in atomic engineering and theory, however, safety was often an afterthought amid the exciting potential of this yet-unexploited
15   resource. The first generation of nuclear scientists comprised true pioneers, and the regions they explored were full of dangers that were known, perhaps, but hadn't been experienced often enough to cause fear.

Substances that spontaneously undergo nuclear fission are called fissile materials, with the most well-known being enriched uranium and plutonium. As the atoms of a fissile substance
20   decay, they radiate (among other particles) neutrons. Each neutron radiated has the potential to split another atom of the substance, and so on, with each split releasing energy and another neutron. If there is enough fissile material arranged in just the right way, each free neutron will go on to split another atom, and so forth, causing a continuous chain reaction, or critical assembly.

Looking back at the origin of atomic weapons research makes it easier to understand how
25   fatal incidents could occur in the name of science, albeit in controlled laboratory or classroom situations. The first nuclear reactor was little more than a pile of uranium dioxide perforated with cadmium control rods (rods that absorb neutrons and thus allow the operator to control the fission). While the experiment sounds mild, know that researchers constructed the unshielded, uncooled stack of fissile uranium, aptly named Chicago Pile-1, beneath the bleachers of a stadium
30   at the University of Chicago—in the middle of a city! Their safety procedure? A man stood at the ready with an axe, waiting nervously to sever the rope suspending the control rods above the pile, should the operators lose control of the chain reaction.

Laboratories did not **condone** inherently dangerous experiments, even in the new atomic age, but accidents still happened. In 1945, Harry Daghlian, a nuclear physicist, was conduct-
35   ing experiments on a plutonium sphere about the size of an orange—a subcritical mass, or an amount of plutonium not large enough to sustain a nuclear chain reaction on its own. Daghlian accidentally dropped a tungsten carbide brick on the sphere. Tungsten functions like a mirror for neutrons, reflecting them back into the mass of plutonium where they split more atoms. The condition caused a critical mass, and from the plutonium came a fatal dose of radiation that killed
40   Daghlian in less than a month.

The very same plutonium sphere that killed Daghlian remained in use at Los Alamos, in spite of its history; one must remember that the effort to isolate plutonium was so costly ($2 billion) that the value of plutonium was tens of thousands of dollars per gram. In 1946, just nine months

after the "demon core" killed Daghlian, a physicist named Louis Slotin used the sphere to conduct
45 critical mass experiments in a room with seven observers, slowly lowering a beryllium hemisphere
onto the demon core with only the tip of a screwdriver preventing the masses from getting too
close together, known also as "tickling the dragon's tail." Because beryllium, like tungsten oxide, is
a neutron reflector, it caused the demon core to approach critical mass as Slotin lowered it while
noting the rapidly rising radiation levels—until he dropped it.

50 An eerie blue flash illuminated the room and observers reported feeling a wave of heat when
the beryllium slipped from Slotin's grasp and closed upon the demon core. Quickly, Slotin
snatched the beryllium away from the critical assembly, stopping the fission—but the damage had
already been done. He had just witnessed his own death blow. Slotin suffered for nine days before
succumbing to the massive dose of radiation. Slotin's body absorbed the bulk of the radiation;
55 though the nearest man was hospitalized, Slotin alone received a lethal dose.

To say that Daghlian or Slotin or any of the pioneer physicists were **dilettantes** who suffered
from "a little learning" would, of course, be the worst type of disinformation; these scientists
probably forgot more nuclear physics knowledge in a week than the average person acquires in
a lifetime. Slotin, though only 35 years old at his death, constructed the Trinity test bomb—the
60 first atomic bomb in the history of mankind. The main oversight in the early atomic age was
not ignorance but complacency. The scientists had experienced a lucky run from the beginning,
bypassing the hazards or mishaps that might have warranted the vigilance necessary to avoid
catastrophe. Lab casualties had been few in spite of the frequent taunting of the nuclear dragon.
Scientists were researching and working with materials that **enthralled** the human race, and that
65 had the potential to end wars and provide electricity to the world. The excitement of the time was
immeasurable—it was a crossroads in history and a celebration of human ingenuity.

1A. The tone of the passage could best be described as
  A.   reverent.
  B.   scathing.
  C.   accurate.
  D.   admiring.
  E.   inhibited.

1B. Choose the phrase from the passage that best supports your answer to question 1A.
  A.   "The first generation of nuclear scientists comprised true pioneers".
  B.   "the excitement of the time was immeasurable"
  C.   "A man stood at the ready with an axe, waiting nervously"
  D.   "Laboratories did not condone inherently dangerous experiments"
  E.   "the pioneer physicists were dilettantes who suffered from 'a little learning' "

2.   The quotation in the introduction is analogous to the phrase,
  A.   "the first generation of atomic scientists were cowboys."
  B.   "research must never impede hands-on experiments."
  C.   "experimenting with unknown forces can be hazardous."
  D.   "there is such a thing as too much knowledge."
  E.   "always know when you are in over your head."

3A. What is the most probable reason for the misleading project and device names?
  A.   The research project was mired in confusing government bureaucracy.
  B.   The Chicago Pile reactor was built in Manhattan.
  C.   The government did not want corporations to make atomic weapons.
  D.   The projects were named for the locations of the laboratories.
  E.   The names were to mislead spies and keep the projects secret.

3B. Choose the phrase from the passage that best supports your answer to question 3A.
    A. "the enigma of harnessing atomic power"
    B. "most massive secret project in all of warfare"
    C. "first generation of nuclear scientists comprised true pioneers"
    D. "like members of a secret atomic cult"
    E. "fatal accidents could occur in the name of science"

4A. The best substitute for the word *terrible*, as it is used in line 6, is
    A. repulsive.
    B. ineffective.
    C. excessive.
    D. unpleasant.
    E. extreme.

4B. Which statement, based on details from the text, best supports your answer to question 4A?
    A. The development of the power came at great monetary expense.
    B. Two scientists were killed while researching atomic power.
    C. Atomic power had to be kept secret, or else it could be used for wrongful purposes.
    D. Just two bombs ended an entire war and began a new historical age.
    E. Atomic bombs were radiation hazards even when they weren't being used.

5A. According to the passage, the particle that is central to sustaining the chain reaction in fission is called a[n]
    A. cadmium.
    B. aluminum.
    C. neutron.
    D. electron.
    E. fission.

5B. If a scientist prevents neutrons from striking additional atoms of fissile material, then
    A. large amounts of radiation will be released.
    B. reflectors will redirect the neutrons toward the fissile material.
    C. the neutrons will create a chain reaction.
    D. the reaction will not become a critical assembly.
    E. the resulting energy release will probably be fatal.

6A. The item referred to as the "demon core" is
    A. the plutonium instrumental in the deaths of two scientists.
    B. the cadmium control rod used to slow fission in Chicago Pile 1.
    C. the beryllium neutron reflector used to create a critical assembly.
    D. the fissile uranium used to build the Trinity bomb.
    E. the laboratory in which two scientists died from radiation poisoning.

6B. Both Daghlian and Slotin were terminally wounded when they
   A.   conducted experiments at the University of Chicago.
   B.   failed to drop control rods into reactors quickly enough.
   C.   spent their entire careers working with radioactive materials.
   D.   lost control of neutron reflectors, causing a release of radiation.
   E.   became too weak to prevent the beryllium from touching the plutonium.

7.   Which of the following situations would not be an example of "tickling the dragon's tail"? (line 47)
   A.   teasing a dog known to bite people
   B.   watching television in the dark for eight hours straight
   C.   swimming in a pool during a severe lightning storm
   D.   walking on a frozen, snow-covered lake in the spring
   E.   investing a large amount of money with a stranger

8A. The author would agree with which one of the following statements?
   A.   Daghlian and Slotin were dangerous renegades among scientists.
   B.   Both Daghlian and Slotin were brilliant scientists.
   C.   What Daghlian and Slotin did was illegal.
   D.   Daghlian and Slotin caused incidents that were more than just accidents.
   E.   Daghlian's mistake was inexcusable, but Slotin's was not.

8B. Which line from the passage contrasts with the author's predominantly positive portrayal of the ill-fated scientists?
   A.   "The main oversight in the early atomic age was not ignorance but complacency."
   B.   "Laboratories did not condone inherently dangerous experiments even in the new atomic age…"
   C.   "To say that Daghlian or Slotin or any of the pioneer physicists were dilettantes who suffered from 'a little learning' would, of course, be the worst type of disinformation…"
   D.   "Slotin, though only 35 years old at his death, constructed the Trinity test bomb—the first atomic bomb in the history of mankind."
   E.   "He had just witnessed his own death blow."

9A. Choose the answer that best describes the organization of the essay.
   A.   increasing importance
   B.   chronological
   C.   cause and effect
   D.   compare and contrast
   E.   problem and solution

9B. The most probable intent of the passage is
   A.   to dissuade the further development of nuclear technology.
   B.   to inform about the risks and sacrifices of new technologies.
   C.   to apologize for the use of atomic bombs.
   D.   to solicit more attention to nuclear research.
   E.   to promote the use of atomic weapons in war.

9C. Of the following choices, which is the most suitable title for this passage?
   A.   Atomic Age Madmen
   B.   The Dawn of Nuclear Energy
   C.   Slotin's Sacrifice
   D.   When the Dragon Bites
   E.   Dangerous Practices

10A. The author's attitude toward the development of nuclear technology is best described as
   A.   supportive.
   B.   skeptical.
   C.   apologetic.
   D.   irrational.
   E.   accusatory.

10B. A recurring motif in the passage warns that the only truly effective method for changing dangerous practices occurs through
   A.   research.
   B.   study.
   C.   experience.
   D.   observation.
   E.   time.

Review Lessons 4-6

Exercise I

Inferences

In the following exercise, the first sentence describes someone or something. Infer information from the first sentence, and then choose the word from the Word Bank that best completes the second sentence.

ostensible	despondent	adamant	appease
connoisseur	diffident	venal	collate

1. The coastal villagers surrendered all the treasure the pirates demanded, only to have the raiders return six months later to demand even more.

   From this sentence, we can infer that the villagers' attempt to _____ the pirates failed.

2. Mrs. Adams, who rarely ever left her house, took her dog for a walk past the home of the new neighbors everyone was talking about.

   From this sentence, we can infer that walking the dog was only a[n] _____ reason for Mrs. Adams's walk.

3. At the fall festival, Mitchell tasted each of the samples of apple cider and then successfully identified which apple species was used to make each one.

   From this sentence, we can infer that Mitchell is a[n] _____ of apple cider.

4. At the office party, Milton, too shy to speak up, stood silently while the cake was passed out, and he was left empty-handed.

   From this sentence, we can infer that _____ people will not get cake at office parties.

5. No matter what his family said, the hoarder refused to throw away the long-expired heaps of canned food strewn around on the garage floor.

   From this sentence, we can infer that the hoarder is _____ about keeping his inedible, old food.

Exercise II

Related Words

Some of the vocabulary words from Lessons 4 through 6 have related meanings. Complete the following sentences by choosing the word that best fits the context, based on information you infer from the use of the italicized word. Some word pairs will be antonyms, some will be synonyms, and some will simply be words often used in the same context.

1. Arthur's _____ remarks were often hurtful and insensitive, but the *credence* of his opinions kept his friends asking for more.
   A. strident
   B. candid
   C. unfettered
   D. cliché
   E. ostensible

2. The widespread *jingoism* quickly waned when the president recommended that the military _____ soldiers from the families of the loudest proponents of the war.
   A. extol
   B. augment
   C. conscript
   D. appease
   E. enthrall

3. To reduce the *disparity* among the little league teams, the coaches _____ less-experienced teams with veteran players.
   A. augmented
   B. imputed
   C. condoned
   D. enthralled
   E. redressed

4. The leader of the creepy _____ that worships insects is always surrounded by a *retinue* of her devoted followers.
   A. chaos
   B. opus
   C. credence
   D. cult
   E. bigot

5. At the monthly meeting of cheese *connoisseurs*, members are known to _____ for hours about perfect cheese blends or the merits of certain aging techniques.
   A. expunge
   B. collate
   C. extol
   D. prate
   E. impute

6. The crash investigator _____ the airplane's malfunction to the *negligence* of a mechanic who had failed to repair a critical control system properly.
   A. conscripted
   B. enthralled
   C. expunged
   D. redressed
   E. imputed

7. Petty Officer Irvin was a mere *dilettante* at nuclear physics, so he did not know the proper _____ required to shut down the submarine's rapidly heating runaway reactor.
   A. chaos
   B. negligence
   C. torpor
   D. protocol
   E. cult

8. *Unfettered* from their electronically locked cages during the power outage, the aggressive chimpanzees escaped and caused _____ in the laboratory, destroying everything in sight.
   A. chaos
   B. torpor
   C. enigma
   D. nuance
   E. jingoism

9. After discovering that the prisoner was, in fact, innocent, the prosecutor _____ his error and *expunged* all accusations from the prisoner's record.
   A. extolled
   B. enthralled
   C. redressed
   D. collated
   E. conscripted

10. The _____ reason for the senator's visit to the soup kitchen was to serve those people living in *privation*, but the visit subsequently created a nice photo opportunity for the politician just before the election.
    A. adamant
    B. cliché
    C. strident
    D. jaunty
    E. ostensible

Exercise III

Deeper Meanings

Choose a word to replace the italicized word in each sentence. All of the possible choices for each sentence have similar definitions, but the correct answer will have a connotation that best suits the context. For example, the words "delete," "destroy," and "obliterate" all mean "to remove or wipe out," but no one would ever say, "I destroyed the name from the document." The correct choice will be the word that has the best specific meaning and does not render the sentence awkward in tone or content. When choices seem close, look for a clue in the context that makes one choice better than the other.

Note that the correct answer is not always the primary vocabulary word from the lesson.

vindictive	candid	venal	sure	noisy
inconsiderate	positive	loud	adamant	blunt
unprincipled	attribute	harsh	blame	

1. Farrah's outspoken comments, while truthful, are so *harsh* that they create more enemies than they do friends.

    Better word: _____

2. A *strident* rumble from the distant mountains alerted the town that the miners were blasting with dynamite that day.

    Better word: _____

3. Willard was *set* that he had seen bigfoot in the woods, but not enough to risk his reputation by telling just anyone.

    Better word: _____

4. I can't *impute* you for turning down the job offer in Iceland for the job in the Caribbean.

    Better word: _____

5. The county government was so *dishonest* that you couldn't even schedule an appointment with the sheriff without bribing the secretary.

    Better word: _____

Exercise IV

Crossword Puzzle

Use the clues to complete the crossword puzzle. The answers consist of vocabulary words from Lessons 4 through 6.

Across

2. total mayhem
5. troublemaking
6. worn out words
7. volunteer someone
10. lazy indifference
11. the right way
12. private helpers
13. work of art
16. add to
17. throw the blame
18. puzzle

Down

1. like fingernails on a chalkboard
3. serious about
4. weekend warrior
8. foodie
9. free to go
14. strange club
15. wants palm grease

Exercise V

Subject Prompts

Here is a writing prompt similar to the one you will find on the writing portion of an assessment test. Follow the instructions below and write a brief, efficient essay.

How much do you value your summer break? When the American school system was established, children spent summers working on the farm, where their help was crucial. Proponents of year-round school claim that this system is antiquated, and that the traditional summer break should be divided up and spread throughout the year. Long breaks, advocates claim, cause students to forget things learned during the school year, and unused, empty school buildings are simply wasteful. Under year-round school, students would have three-week extended breaks throughout the year, as well as all the traditional holiday breaks.

Detractors of the year-round school system note that it will challenge extracurricular programs and summer jobs, and that the breaks would still be long enough for students to forget what they have learned. Supporters point to the success of existing year-round schools in use in many states and nations.

Imagine that your school is contemplating a switch to year-round education (or reverting back to a traditional school year with a summer break, if it is already a year-round school). Take a position, and write a well-crafted letter to the school board using reasons and examples to support your opinion.

Thesis: Write a *one-sentence* response to the above assignment. Make certain this single sentence offers a clear statement of your position.

Example: If school is truly a preparation for adult life, then students should be attending it all year, as though they were working.

_____

_____

Organizational Plan: List at least three subtopics you will use to support your main idea. This list is your outline.

1. _____

2. _____

3. _____

Draft: Following your outline, write a good first draft of your essay. Remember to support all your points with examples, facts, references to reading, etc.

Review and Revise: Exchange essays with a classmate. Using the scoring guide for Development on page 258, score your partner's essay (while he or she scores yours). Focus on the development of ideas and the use of language conventions. If necessary, rewrite your essay to incorporate more (or more relevant) support and/or improve your use of language.

Lesson Seven

1. **transpose** (tran spōz´) *v.* to change the order or place of, especially letters, words, or musical notes
   The composer *transposed* the trumpet score so that it would be suitable to play on a French horn.
   syn: shift; reorder

2. **dilemma** (di lem´ ə) *n.* a choice between two unpleasant or difficult options
   Whether to repair my old car or purchase a new one was a real *dilemma*.

3. **sardonic** (sar don´ ik) *adj.* using mocking or scornful humor
   Ken made the *sardonic* observation that strip searching the 80-year-old passenger at the airport will save the nation from terrorists.
   syn: cynical; sarcastic   *ant: optimistic*

4. **intern** (in´ turn) *n.* a student or recent graduate working as an apprentice while learning a job
   As an *intern* learning to become a surgeon, Tyler spent months assisting the hospital's emergency room doctor.

5. **ambivalent** (am biv´ ə lənt) *adj.* having opposing attitudes or feelings toward a person, thing, or idea; unable to decide
   Doug felt *ambivalent* about his job; although he hated the pressure, he loved the challenge.
   syn: uncertain; wavering   *ant: certain; resolute*

6. **destitute** (des´ ti tōōt) *adj.* extremely poor; lacking necessities like food and shelter
   Because they had no insurance, they were left *destitute* when their house burned down.
   syn: impoverished; penniless   *ant: affluent*

7. **demure** (di mūr´) *adj.* quiet and modest; reserved
   Her *demure* behavior was really a ruse to cover up her criminal nature.
   syn: prim   *ant: indiscreet*

8. **intrepid** (in trep´ əd) *adj.* without fear; brave
   The *intrepid* warrior did not even flinch when the tiger leapt from the tree.
   syn: bold; fearless   *ant: cowardly*

9. **affront** (a frunt´) *n.* an outrageous insult, often public
The challenger hoped that his *affront* toward the champion would lure him into a new bout for the title.
syn: offense; slight   *ant: praise*

10. **erudite** (er´ yə dīt) *adj.* scholarly; learned
Not much of a scholar, Justin was intimidated by his *erudite* girlfriend.
syn: educated   *ant: unlettered; illiterate*

11. **culmination** (kul mə nā´ shən) *n.* the highest point of attainment; the end or climax
Winning the state tournament was the *culmination* of a great basketball season.
syn: apex   *ant: nadir*

12. **rend** (rend) *v.* to tear apart violently
The toddler tried to *rend* her father's eyeglasses with tiny iron fists until he distracted her with a cookie.
syn: rip; rive

13. **demagogue** (dem´ ə gäg) *n.* a leader who appeals to citizens' emotions to obtain power
The *demagogue* evoked the sympathy of the public to justify his crimes in office.
syn: rabble-rouser

14. **concur** (kən kûr´) *v.* to be of the same opinion; to agree with
I *concur* that we should keep this meeting short.
syn: support; agree   *ant: dispute; differ*

15. **lobby** (lo´ bē) *v.* to try to persuade officials to support or reject a cause
Ed *lobbied* congress to change the new tax law that threatened to ruin his business.

Exercise I

Words in Context

From the list below, supply the words needed to complete the paragraph. Some words will not be used.

concur	intrepid	sardonic	destitute
dilemma	ambivalent	culmination	

1. One year after the _____ of the second Mineral War, the surviving inhabitants of the Europa mining colony were _____ and malnourished. The chief engineer tried her best to restore the food reprocessing system, but, owing to the lack of replacement parts, the unit could produce only thirty percent of the colony's nutritional needs. Captain Keith remained _____ about leading a few _____ miners on a necessary but dangerous expedition to the old generation plant in the Nova Crater to salvage parts for the rapidly declining life support system. Most of the miners were making _____ quips about their fate at the colony, and Captain Keith would have been lying if he said that he didn't _____ with their pessimistic opinions.

From the list below, supply the words needed to complete the paragraph. Some words will not be used.

culmination	demagogue	concur	erudite
dilemma	demure		

2. Clayton surprised everyone in Selbyville when he entered the race for mayor. For twenty-six years, he had been the mild-mannered, _____ clerk at the Selbyville Courthouse. Well-versed in history and politics, the _____ Clayton never really struck anyone as having the type of personality required to win an election, let alone become the mayor. Word spread quickly when, during a special pre-election meeting, Clayton stood at the podium and delivered an impressive speech. Every word was loaded with passion, especially when Clayton addressed Selbyville's _____ of accepting or rejecting a controversial landfill. After ten minutes of rhetoric, Clayton had the townspeople shouting their support, and the sentiment continued right through to the election, after which Clayton became the new mayor. Three months later, the citizens of Selbyville discovered that Clayton was just a[n] _____ when construction of the new landfill began, and he mysteriously bought a new speedboat that was well beyond the range of a typical small-town mayor's salary.

From the list below, supply the words needed to complete the paragraph. Some words will not be used.

affront	**intern**	**rend**	**dilemma**
transpose	**lobby**	**sardonic**	

3. Carmen was only a[n] _____ at her company, still learning the job, but she knew that she could not allow a dangerous situation to continue, whether or not it would be a[n] _____ to her supervisor. Going over her boss's head, Carmen _____ management to adopt a safer procedure on the production line before one of the workers got killed or seriously injured. The change would not be costly; Carmen recommended that the company should simply _____ a few steps in the assembly line, leaving the most hazardous processes for the end, when fewer workers would be present. At first, Carmen worried that her assertion would _____ her dream of a career as an industrial engineer; to her surprise, the company instead offered her a full-time job.

Exercise II

Sentence Completion

Complete the sentence in a way that shows you understand the meaning of the italicized vocabulary word.

1. Marc decided to *lobby* the government in order to…

2. When forced to be in public, the *demure* Kelly…

3. It was an *affront* to say that the popular candidate was…

4. Now *destitute*, the bankrupt stockbroker lives…

5. A *dilemma* at work can force a person to…

6. Manny was *ambivalent* about taking the new job because…

7. Your *sardonic* sense of humor causes…

8. Stranded behind enemy lines, the *intrepid* soldier…

9. Mischievous kids *transposed* the words on the restaurant sign to say…

10. A *demagogue* like Hitler can successfully convince people to…

11. His parents would not *concur* with Dharma's decision to…

12. The *culmination* of the symphony's season occurred at…

13. Connor *rended* the letter that said…

14. The *erudite* professor occasionally lost the attention of her students because…

15. Until the *intern* becomes certified as a doctor, she is not allowed to…

Exercise III

Roots, Prefixes, and Suffixes

Study the entries and answer the questions that follow.

The root *fid* means "faith" or "trust."
The root *form* means "shape."
The root *crea* means "create, make."
The suffix *–tion* means "the act of."
The prefix *re–* means "back" or "again."
The prefix *con–* means "with."

1. Using *literal* translations as guidance, define the following words without using a dictionary:

   A. reformation   D. re-creation
   B. reverted   E. fidelity
   C. malformed   F. confide

2. *Infidelity* is _____.

3. The Marine Corps' motto, "Semper Fidelis," means _____
   _____.

4. List as many words as you can think of that contain the roots *fid* and *form*.

Exercise IV

Inference

Complete the sentence by inferring information about the italicized word from its context.

1. During the battle, the *intrepid* soldier will probably volunteer to…

2. When Cynthia sees a *destitute* child, she usually…

3. If a *demagogue* gets elected, the citizens might…

Exercise V

Writing

Here is a writing prompt similar to the one you will find on the writing portion of an assessment test.

Plan and write an essay on the following statement:

> They that can give up essential liberty to obtain a little temporary safety deserve neither liberty nor safety.
>
> –Benjamin Franklin
> *Historical Review of Pennsylvania*, 1759

Assignment: In a well-organized essay, refute or defend Franklin's point of view. Be certain to support your position by discussing an example (or examples) from current events, science and technology, or your own experience and observation.

Thesis: Write a *one-sentence* response to the above assignment. Make certain this single sentence offers a clear statement of your position.

Example: When the nation is at high risk of attack, the government should be allowed to create temporary policies to aid in defense, even if they restrict certain liberties.

-or-

Our government cannot establish any laws that undermine our civil liberties, regardless of the degree of threat to our country.

_____

_____

Organizational Plan: List at least three subtopics you will use to support your main idea. This list is your outline.

1. _____

2. _____

3. _____

Draft: Following your outline, write a good first draft of your essay. Remember to support all your points with examples, facts, references to reading, etc.

Review and Revise: Exchange essays with a classmate. Using the scoring guide for Word Choice on page 261, score your partner's essay (while he or she scores yours). Focus on word choice and the use of language conventions. If necessary, rewrite your essay to improve word choice and/or your use of language.

Exercise VI

Improving Paragraphs

Read the following passage and then choose the best revision for the underlined portions of the para-
graph. The questions will require you to make decisions regarding the revision of the reading selection.
Some revisions are not of actual mistakes, but will improve the clarity of the writing.

[1]

When you see a marathon runner stumble across the finish line, exhausted after a journey
that would cause the average person to keel over dead, do you "say so what! Anyone can do that?"[1]
Maybe you wouldn't. But, many[2] people would assert that yes, anyone can do it, and, as a matter
of fact, we are made for it.

1. A. NO CHANGE
    B. say "So what!": anyone can do that?
    C. say "So what! anyone can do that".
    D. say, "So what! Anyone can do that"?

2. F. NO CHANGE
    G. wouldn't, but many
    H. would not; therefore,
    J. wouldn't. But many

[2]

We don't have sharp claws or long teeth to catch food or defend ourselves from predators.
Sure, we have the most biggest[4] brains, but our average eyesight and hearing are still likely to
get us into situations in which those mammals having claws, teeth, and an abundance of muscle
make short work of us. Their is only one thing that human beings can do better than the wild
mammals: run.[5] And not fast, either—certainly any bear or leopard will catch you before you even
turn around; though animals will outrun humans in a sprint, however, they tire very quickly, and
that's when humans gain the advantage. It's the long run at which we excel,[6] mainly because we
are built for it.

3. Which of the following sentences would be the most appropriate introductory
    sentence for paragraph 2?
    A. No one can question the ability of long distance runners in comparison to
        most predators.
    B. In comparison to the average mammal, a person's physical ability may not
        seem especially impressive.
    C. In a comparison between humans and other mammals, people are not
        especially impressive.
    D. Modern footwear, some runners attest, is conducive to foot injury over
        long distances.

4. F. NO CHANGE
    G. the bigger
    H. the most
    J. the biggest

5. A. NO CHANGE
    B. There are many things that human beings can do better than wild mammals, and one of the best talents we have is running.
    C. One of the things that human beings can do better than wild mammals is run.
    D. There is only one thing that human beings can do better than wild mammals can: run.

6. F. NO CHANGE
    G. It is in the long run at which we excel,
    H. The long distance running is where we excel,
    J. We excel in the long run, distance running,

[3]

People, unlike most beasts, have the ability to sweat. Coupled with our hairless skin, sweating allows people to keep their body temperature down during long periods of effort. Our <u>cooling, ability, large knees, and elastic tendons</u>,[7] allow us to outrun a horse—in the long run, of course. That's right: over long distances, human beings can outrun almost every running mammal on earth. This ability might not have saved our ancestors from saber tooth tigers, but it provided them a distinct advantage <u>while tracking the many tasty quadrupeds living on the plains</u>.[8]

7. A. NO CHANGE
    B. cooling ability, large, knees and elastic tendons,
    C. ability to cool large knees and elastic tendons
    D. cooling ability, large knees, and elastic tendons

8. F. NO CHANGE
    G. while tracking the quadrupeds, many of which were tasty, living on the plains.
    H. while tracking the tasty plains animals.
    J. while they tracked down animals, which they knew were tasty, on the plains.

[4]

Antelope, like dogs, simply do not sweat; they must pant to cool their bodies. In order to pant, an animal must stop running. Animals that are being chased by hungry people with spears do not have the luxury <u>to rest and thus overheat and collapse</u>,[9] rendering themselves easy targets for the brain-guided clubs and arrows of our jogging ancestors. To see the process for yourself, visit the Bushmen of the Kalahari Desert and follow them on a hunt, which may continue for miles over the course of days. Be sure to keep up.

9.   A. NO CHANGE
  _ B. to rest and overheat and collapse
     C. of rest; then overheat and collapse
     D. of resting and, thus, overheat and collapse

[5]

When one returns from the Kalahari, you should swing[10] by the Copper Canyon of Mexico, where the Tarahumara people play a game that involves running in a group more than fifty miles, kicking a wooden ball all the way. Leave your sneakers at home: the Tarahumara run virtually barefoot, shod in simple one-piece sandals made from thin strips of leather or rubber. The lack of overengineered footwear among the Tarahumara, especially over unpaved, natural surfaces, allows the machine of the human body to do the job it is already[11] perfectly adapted to do.

10. F. NO CHANGE
     G. When returning from the Kalahari, he should swing
     H. When returning from the Kalahari, swing
     J. Returning from the Kalahari you should swing

11. A. NO CHANGE
     B. it's now
     C. it is all ready
     D. it can be

[6]

Oddly enough, foot and leg injuries common to runners in the developed world—joint damage, shin splints, bone spurs—are practically unknown to the Tarahumara. Sneakers typically force runners to land on their heels, sending shocks throughout the body. While making[12] minimal use of the springlike arch and large tendons of the foot. Barefoot runners land midfoot, allowing their bodies to absorb the shock and return the energy to the stride. Granted, barefoot running on manmade surfaces might be devastating to feet; people,[13] after all, didn't spend 100,000 years adapting to run on blacktop and pavement.

12. F. NO CHANGE
     G. body; while making
     H. body, while making
     J. body—while making

13. A. NO CHANGE
     B. devastating to feet! people
     C. devastating to feet—People
     D. devastating to feet, people

[7]

Now, before you go out and run a marathon, know that long-distance runners don't <u>sit around for four months in between twenty-mile jaunts being sedentary and not doing anything</u>.[14] Predictably, people who run long distances can do so because they do it regularly. Most human beings might have the potential to run long distances, but that potential is not going to be actualized by couch potatofxtres or people who run one mile in order to loosen up for a workout. There isn't an easy way to achieve the constitution and endurance of a distance runner—<u>naturals or not, we still have to work up to it</u>.[15]

14. F. NO CHANGE
    G. sit around being sedentary for four months in between twenty-mile jaunts and not doing anything.
    H. sit around for four months in between twenty-mile jaunts not doing any thing.
    J. sit around for four months in between twenty-mile jaunts.

15. A. NO CHANGE
    B. natural runners or not, humans still must work up to it.
    C. natural or not, we still have to work up to a marathon.
    D. natural runners or not, we must still work up to running a marathon.

Lesson Eight

1. **duplicity** (dōō plis´ i tē) *n.* intentional deceit in speech or conduct
His *duplicity* became obvious when he absent-mindedly arranged to meet both his
wife and his mistress at the same restaurant.
syn: deception   *ant: straightforwardness*

2. **belie** (bi lī´) *v.* to falsely represent
Tara's yawn *belied* her genuine interest in the concert.
syn: contradict; misrepresent   *ant: prove; show*

3. **droll** (drōl) *adj.* amusing in an odd or whimsical way
Xander had a *droll* manner of telling stories that kept everyone entertained.
syn: quaint

4. **abate** (ə bāt´) *v.* to lessen in violence or intensity
When the winds *abated*, the helicopter was able to land.
syn: subside; decrease   *ant: intensify; increase*

5. **glib** (glib) *adj.* performed with such ease and skill as to appear insincere
Andy's *glib* apology to his sister seemed too easy for it to have been genuine.
syn: slick; artful   *ant: sincere*

6. **abhor** (ab hôr´) *v.* to detest; to hate strongly
I *abhor* doing my laundry, so I have it professionally cleaned.
syn: despise; loathe   *ant: love; adore*

7. **journeyman** (jûr´ nē mən) *n.* a fully trained and qualified worker
Mark was a *journeyman* for twenty years before he gained enough skills to be
promoted to craftsman.
                                                    ant: apprentice; neophyte

8. **dole** (dōl) *v.* to distribute; to give out sparingly
At the crowded Red Cross shelter, food was *doled* out carefully to the earthquake
victims.
                                                    ant: hoard

9. **protean** (prō´ tē ən) *adj.* readily changeable in form, shape, or meaning
The international spy maintained a *protean* identity that enabled her to adapt to and
succeed in almost any situation imaginable, anywhere in the world.
syn: versatile; mutable   *ant: fixed*

10. **gamut** (gam´ ət) *n.* the whole range or extent
Carmela's *gamut* of friends includes both overzealous socialists and greedy capitalists.

11. **decorum** (di kôr´ əm) *n.* conformity to accepted standards of conduct; proper behavior
The usually restless toddler surprised everyone with his *decorum* during the ceremony.
syn: propriety   *ant: inappropriateness*

12. **extrovert** (ek´ strə vûrt) *n.* one who is outgoing; one who is energized rather than drained by interactions with others
As an *extrovert*, Liz loved parties and preferred entertaining to spending a quiet night alone.
ant: introvert

13. **propagate** (pro´ pə gāt) *v.* to spread or transmit, especially by reproduction
The computer virus *propagated* itself and caused the hard drive to fail.

14. **effigy** (ef´ i jē) *n.* a crude dummy or image representing a hated person or group
The repressed people burned an *effigy* of their tyrannous ruler.

15. **austere** (ô stîr´) *adj.* stern; severe; plain
The judge was as *austere* in her courtroom manner as she was in her lifestyle and dress.
syn: strict; unadorned   *ant: luxurious; indulgent*

Exercise I

Words in Context

From the list below, supply the words needed to complete the paragraph. Some words will not be used.

¹ droll	³ gamut	⁵ effigy	⁷ austere
² duplicity	⁴ abhor	⁶ extrovert	

1. Monique was a[n] _____**6**_____ who loved dealing with people, but she never thought that she would satisfy her need for socializing by selling used cars. She always _____**3 4**_____ salespeople, but after becoming one, Monique realized that only a fraction of the salespeople indulged in the _____**1 2**_____ and false promises that make dissatisfied customers angry enough to burn _____**5**_____ of them. In fact, she enjoyed running through the _____**3**_____ of sales techniques needed to close the deal.

From the list below, supply the words needed to complete the paragraph. Some words will not be used.

~~¹ abate~~	~~³ decorum~~	⁵ dole	ᴺ abhor
~~² droll~~	~~⁴ austere~~	~~⁶ duplicity~~	

2. Typhoon Paka hammered the island of Guam for twelve hours before the winds _____**1**_____. Gusts over one hundred fifty miles an hour devastated the previously green island, creating _____**4**_____ living conditions for residents in the weeks to come, especially for the estimated five thousand people who lost their homes. Residents able to witness Paka in action were astounded by the serious but almost _____**2**_____ sight of Paka's invisible forces tossing around automobiles, dumpsters, and palm trees as though they were children's toys. In the days following Paka, residents adhered to traditional post-typhoon _____**3**_____ by cleaning up hundreds of tons of debris, checking on the condition of friends and neighbors, repairing property, and, because of the lack of electricity, hosting mass barbecues before food perished in warm refrigerators. Luckily, food was not in short supply, but water had to be _____**5**_____ out by several agencies in the weeks following the tempest.

From the list below, supply the words needed to complete the paragraph. Some words will not be used.

¹ ~~glib~~	³ decorum	⁵ ~~protean~~	⁷ ~~journeyman~~
² extrovert	⁴ ~~belie~~	⁶ ~~propagate~~	

3. In only two weeks, the disease outbreak _____**6**_____ beyond the borders of its initial region to four continents. The _____**5**_____ bacteria responsible was often missed by medical _____**7**_____ in lab tests because it often changes in appearance and resembles other harmless strains of bacteria. The rampant purchase of vaccines _____**4**_____ the false bravado of critics who offered _____**1**_____ dismissals of the threat of deadly germs.

Exercise II

Sentence Completion

Complete the sentence in a way that shows you understand the meaning of the italicized vocabulary word.

1. Too many monkeys were *propagating* in the zoo, so... They Shot them

2. The peasants burned the *effigy* of the Duke because... They didn't like him

3. The factory foreman expected *journeymen* to be capable of... working

4. The epidemic finally *abated*, and the doctors... ran and Jumped

5. Having no time for *decorum*, the federal agents charged into the ballroom and... danced

6. Three days after the shipwreck, the captain *doled* out... food

7. The comedian's *droll* attempt to impersonate the president caused... laughter

8. The *protean* lab-created organ tissue will be able to... last longer

9. The *austere* conditions on the Alaskan tundra caused the settlers to... build shelter

10. The *gamut* of people on the elevator ran from... The Dino Saur

11. Othello trusted his wife until Iago's *duplicity* made the Moor think that... he was cheating

12. Kenyon, an *extrovert*, called all her friends and... Parents

13. Mary *belied* her vast knowledge of history when she... took the test

14. I did *abhor* violence, so I never... fought

15. No one believed the boss's *glib* apology for... Murdering the People

Exercise III

Roots, Prefixes, and Suffixes

Study the entries and answer the questions that follow.

The roots *frag* and *fract* mean "break."
The root *chrono* means "time."
The suffix *–ment* means "the result of" or "product of the action."
The suffix *–logical* means "ordered by."
The prefix *re–* means "back, again."

1. Using *literal* translations as guidance, define the following words without using a dictionary:

   A. chronic   D. chronological
   B. fragment   E. chronicle
   C. fragile   F. refract

2. A character answering a telephone during the play *Julius Caesar* would be an *anachronism* because _____.

3. A *fragmentary* report is one that is _____.

4. List as many words as you can think of that contain the forms *frag, fract,* and *chrono.*

Exercise IV

Inference

Complete the sentence by inferring information about the italicized word from its context.

1. If you *abhor* getting muddy and dirty, then you should probably not…

2. As the wagon train moved west, conditions on the plains became so *austere* that the pioneers…

3. To fashion a detailed *effigy* of the mayor, the angry townspeople might…

Exercise V

Critical Reading

Below is a pair of reading passages followed by several multiple-choice questions. Carefully read the passages and choose the best answer for each of the questions.

Both of these passages are arguments in favor of the American War of Independence against Great Britain. The first comes from the initial pamphlet in Thomas Paine's series entitled The American Crisis, *which uses emotional appeals to persuade the reader. The second comes from the Declaration of Independence, which takes on a more rational, logical aspect.*

Passage 1

These are the times that try men's souls. The summer soldier and the sunshine patriot will in this crisis, shrink from the service of his country; but he that stands it NOW, deserves the love and thanks of man and woman. Tyranny, like hell, is not easily conquered; yet we have this consolation with us, that the harder the conflict, the more glorious the triumph. What we obtain too cheap,
5   we esteem too lightly; 'tis dearness only that gives everything its proper value. Heaven knows how to put a proper price upon its goods; and it would be strange indeed, if so celestial an article as FREEDOM should not be highly rated. Britain, with an army to enforce her tyranny, has declared that she has a right (not only to TAX), but "to BIND us in ALL CASES WHATSOEVER," and if being bound in that manner is not slavery then is there not such a thing as slavery upon earth.
10 Even the expression is impious, for so unlimited a power can belong only to God....

I have as little superstition in me as any man living, but my secret opinion has ever been, and still is, that God Almighty will not give up a people to military destruction, or leave them unsupportedly to perish, who have so earnestly and so repeatedly sought to avoid the calamities of war, by every decent method which wisdom could invent. Neither have I so much of the infidel in me,
15 as to suppose that He has relinquished the government of the world, and given us up to the care of devils; and as I do not, I cannot see on what grounds the king of Britain can look up to heaven for help against us: a common murderer, a highwayman, or housebreaker, has as good a pretense as he....

I once felt all that kind of anger, which a man ought to feel, against the mean principles that
20 are held by the Tories: a noted one, who kept a tavern at Amboy, was standing at his door, with as pretty a child in his hand, about eight or nine years old, as I ever saw, and after speaking his mind as freely as he thought was prudent, finished with this unfatherly expression, "Well! Give me peace in my day." Not a man lives on the continent but fully believes that a separation must some time or other finally take place, and a generous parent should have said, "If there must be
25 trouble, let it be in my day, that my child may have peace"; and this single reflection, well applied, is sufficient to awaken every man to duty. Not a place upon earth might be so happy as America. Her situation is remote from all the wrangling world, and she has nothing to do but to trade with them. A man can distinguish himself between temper and principle, and I am as confident, as I am that God governs the world, that America will never be happy till she gets clear of foreign
30 dominion. Wars, without ceasing, will break out till that period arrives, and the continent must in the end be conqueror; for though the flame of liberty may sometimes cease to shine, the coal can never expire.

Let it be told to the future world, that in the depth of winter, when nothing but hope and virtue could survive, that the city and the country, alarmed at one common danger, came forth to
35 meet and to repulse it. Say not that thousands are gone, turn out your tens of thousands; throw not the burden of the day upon Providence, but "show your faith by your works," that God may bless you. It matters not where you live, or what rank of life you hold, the evil or the blessing will reach you all. The far and the near, the home counties and the back, the rich and the poor, will

40 suffer or rejoice alike. The heart that feels not now is dead; the blood of his children will curse his cowardice, who shrinks back at a time when a little might have saved the whole, and made them happy. I love the man that can smile in trouble, that can gather strength from distress, and grow brave by reflection. 'Tis the business of little minds to shrink; but he whose heart is firm, and whose conscience approves his conduct, will pursue his principles unto death. My own line of reasoning is to myself as straight and clear as a ray of light. Not all the treasures of the world,

45 so far as I believe, could have induced me to support an offensive war, for I think it murder; but if a thief breaks into my house, burns and destroys my property, and kills or threatens to kill me, or those that are in it, and to "bind me in all cases whatsoever" to his absolute will, am I to suffer it? What signifies it to me, whether he who does it is a king or a common man; my countryman or not my countryman; whether it be done by an individual villain, or an army of them?

Passage 2

When in the Course of human events, it becomes necessary for one people to dissolve the political bands which have connected them with another, and to assume among the powers of the earth, the separate and equal station to which the Laws of Nature and of Nature's God entitle them, a decent respect to the opinions of mankind requires that they should declare the causes

5 which impel them to the separation....

The history of the present King of Great Britain is a history of repeated injuries and usurpations, all having in direct object the establishment of absolute Tyranny over these States. To prove this, let facts be submitted to a candid world.

He has refused his Assent to Laws the most wholesome and necessary for the public good.

10 He has forbidden his Governors to pass Laws of immediate and pressing importance, unless suspended in their operation till his Assent should be obtained; and when so suspended, he has utterly neglected to attend to them.

He has refused to pass other Laws for the accommodation of large districts of people, unless those people would relinquish the right of Representation in the Legislature, a right inestimable

15 to them and formidable to tyrants only.

He has called together legislative bodies at places unusual, uncomfortable, and distant from the depository of their Public Records, for the sole purpose of fatiguing them into compliance with his measures....

He has erected a multitude of New Offices, and sent hither swarms of officers to harass our

20 people and eat out their substance.

He has dissolved Representative Houses repeatedly, for opposing with manly firmness his invasions on the rights of the people....

He has plundered our seas, ravaged our coasts, burnt our towns, and destroyed the lives of our people.

25 He is at this time transporting large Armies of foreign Mercenaries to complete the works of death, desolation, and tyranny, already begun with circumstances of Cruelty & Perfidy scarcely paralleled in the most barbarous ages, and totally unworthy the Head of a civilized nation.

He has constrained our fellow Citizens taken Captive on the high Seas to bear Arms against their Country, to become the executioners of their friends and Brethren, or to fall themselves by

30 their Hands....

In every stage of these Oppressions We have Petitioned for Redress in the most humble terms: Our repeated Petitions have been answered only by repeated injury. A Prince, whose character is thus marked by every act which may define a Tyrant, is unfit to be the ruler of a free people.

Nor have We been wanting in attentions to our British brethren. We have warned them from

35 time to time of attempts by their legislature to extend an unwarrantable jurisdiction over us. We have reminded them of the circumstances of our emigration and settlement here. We have appealed to their native justice and magnanimity, and we have conjured them by the ties of our common kindred to disavow these usurpations, which would inevitably interrupt our connections and correspondence. They too have been deaf to the voice of justice and of consanguinity.

40 We must, therefore, acquiesce in the necessity, which denounces our Separation, and hold them,

as we hold the rest of mankind, Enemies in War, in Peace Friends.

We, therefore, the Representatives of the united States of America, in General Congress, Assembled, appealing to the Supreme Judge of the world for the rectitude of our intentions, do, in the Name, and by Authority of the good People of these Colonies, solemnly publish and declare,
45   That these united Colonies are, and of Right ought to be Free and Independent States, that they are Absolved from all Allegiance to the British Crown, and that all political connection between them and the State of Great Britain, is and ought to be totally dissolved; and that as Free and Independent States, they have full Power to levy War, conclude Peace, contract Alliances, establish Commerce, and to do all other Acts and Things which Independent States may of right do. — And
50   for the support of this Declaration, with a firm reliance on the protection of Divine Providence, we mutually pledge to each other our Lives, our Fortunes, and our sacred Honor.

1A. In the context of the first passage, what is the most appropriate definition of *dearness*, as it appears in line 5?
    A.   fondness
    B.   expense
    C.   endearment
    D.   glory
    E.   courage

1B. Choose the statement that best rephrases the sentence, "What we obtain too cheap, we esteem too lightly" (passage 1, lines 4-5).
    A.   Necessity is the mother of invention.
    B.   Garbage in, garbage out.
    C.   Practice makes perfect.
    D.   Easy come, easy go.
    E.   The value of the trip is the journey itself.

2A. In the first passage, the purpose of the simile in line 3 is most likely
    A.   to honor the religious occasion of this essay.
    B.   to show the ease with which the Americans would defeat Britain.
    C.   to give the argument a sharply moral tone.
    D.   to introduce the difficulty of overcoming temptation.
    E.   to add the rhetorical weight of an expletive to the sentence.

2B. Choose the line from the passage that contains another instance that supports your answer to question 2A.
    A.   " 'Tis the business of little minds to shrink"
    B.   "The far and the near, the home counties and the back, the rich and the poor, will suffer or rejoice alike"
    C.   "Not a place upon earth might be so happy as America"
    D.   "I cannot see on what grounds the king of Britain can look up to heaven for help against us"
    E.   "If there must be trouble, let it be in my day, that my child may have peace"

3A. The overall tone of the first passage can best be described as
   A. logical.
   B. hysterical.
   C. pessimistic.
   D. alarmed.
   E. practical.

3B. Which pair of words does not describe an example of extremes in the first paragraph of passage 1?
   A. darkness and daylight
   B. freedom and slavery
   C. good and evil
   D. cowardice and heroics
   E. difficulty and ease

4A. As suggested by the author, the Tories mentioned in passage 1, line 20, are people who would
   A. leave their families and heed their nation's call when needed.
   B. force their own children to fight for the king.
   C. accept the costs of securing liberty for America.
   D. rather fight now than see the conflict pass on to their children.
   E. disagree with the author's insistence on going to war with Great Britain.

4B. The author's condemnation of the Tory father's selfishness in passage 1 depends on the premise that
   A. war can be avoided.
   B. the king will surrender.
   C. peace cannot be obtained for the next generation.
   D. diplomatic solutions to the crisis have not been exhausted.
   E. war is inevitable.

5A. Who is the primary audience of passage 2?
   A. the American colonists
   B. the king of England
   C. the American press
   D. the French ambassador
   E. the world at large

5B. Which phrase from passage 2 best supports your answer to question 5A?
   A. "…let facts be submitted to a candid world."
   B. "The history of the present King of Great Britain is a history of repeated injuries."
   C. "Nor have We been wanting in attentions to our British brethren."
   D. "A Prince…is unfit to be the ruler of a free people"
   E. "…we mutually pledge to each other our Lives, our Fortunes, and our sacred Honor."

6. What can be inferred from the following statement from passage 2?
    "A Prince, whose character is thus marked by every act which may define a Tyrant, is unfit to be the ruler of a free people."
    A. Royalty in any form is symbolic of oppression and cannot be tolerated.
    B. The king's detractors are a minority among the American population.
    C. Even a good king would not be tolerable to freedom-loving people.
    D. Independence would not have been necessary had the king been a good ruler.
    E. Leadership of colonies falls outside the duties of a king.

7A. As it is used in line 39, the word *consanguinity* most nearly means
    A. surrender.
    B. relationship.
    C. discussion.
    D. treachery.
    E. war.

7B. Which phrase from the context of *consanguinity* best supports your answer to question 7A?
    A. "unwarrantable jurisdiction"
    B. "appealed to their native justice"
    C. "Enemies in War, in Peace Friends"
    D. "circumstances of our emigration"
    E. "by the ties of our common kindred"

8. Which word below is used in the second passage to portray the British representatives as less than human?
    A. dissolved (line 47)
    B. substance (line 20)
    C. swarms (line 19)
    D. burnt (line 23)
    E. repeated (line 32)

9A. Which of the following statements best describes the difference between the rhetorical strategy of the passages?
    A. Passage 1 appeals more to the logic of the reader than passage 2 does.
    B. Passage 1 engages the reader emotionally much more than passage 2 does.
    C. Passage 1 details the misdeeds of the British king, while passage 2 is a warning.
    D. Passage 2 avoids reference to divine intervention, while passage 1 invokes God's aid on behalf of the American cause.
    E. Passage 1 uses shorter sentences to increase the emotional pace, while passage 2 seems to be written for a more intellectual audience.

9B. Which emotionally charged subject appears in passage 1, but not in the context of passage 2?
  A.   death
  B.   God
  C.   betrayal
  D.   tyranny
  E.   children

10A. Choose the statement that best describes the difference in intent between the passages.
  A.   Passage 1 petitions for support; passage 2 declares the conflict valid.
  B.   Passage 1 argues for peace; passage 2 declares peace.
  C.   Passage 1 lists crimes of the king; passage 2 list crimes of the king's soldiers.
  D.   Passage 1 sympathizes with Tories; passage 2 criminalizes them.
  E.   Passage 1 argues for war against Tories; passage 2 declares war on the king.

10B. Passage 1 most resembles which one of the following types of content?
  A.   a council meeting
  B.   a general's surrender
  C.   a journal entry
  D.   an award acceptance speech
  E.   a coach's pep talk

10C. Choose the phrase from passage 1 that best summarizes the motive behind passage 2.
  A.   "...so unlimited a power can belong only to God."
  B.   "Not a place upon earth might be so happy as America."
  C.   "...America will never be happy till she gets clear of foreign dominion."
  D.   "...though the flame of liberty may sometimes cease to shine, the coal can never expire."
  E.   "These are the times that try men's souls."

Lesson Nine

1. **sere** (sēr) *adj.* dry and withered
   After two weeks without water, the *sere* plant broke at the stem.
   syn: desiccated; arid   *ant: lush*

2. **heinous** (hā´ nəs) *adj.* hatefully or shockingly evil
   The jury was shocked by the young woman's *heinous* crimes.
   syn: abhorrent; horrid

3. **enhance** (en hans´) *v.* to increase the value or beauty of something
   The soft, shimmering moonlight *enhanced* the beauty of the sparkling lake.
   syn: improve; heighten   *ant: diminish; decrease*

4. **unctuous** (ungk´chōō əs) *adj.* exaggeratedly or insincerely polite
   The salesman kept calling me "ma'am" in such an *unctuous* tone that I did
   not trust him for a minute.
   syn: oily   *ant: genuine; sincere*

5. **magnanimous** (mag nan´ ə məs) *adj.* noble; generous in forgiving; free from
     petty feelings or acts
   Allowing the man who had insulted him to stay for dinner was a *magnanimous*
   gesture on Robert's part.
   syn: generous   *ant: petty; mean*

6. **postulate** (pos´ tu lāt) *v.* to assume or claim as true, especially when arguing
   The speech therapist *postulated* that the woman's tongue ring interfered with her
   enunciation.
   syn: presume; suppose

7. **contrite** (kən trīt´) *adj.* feeling regret for having committed some wrongdoing
   The *contrite* child wished she had never thought of playing baseball near the
   greenhouse.
   syn: repentant; remorseful   *ant: shameless; unrepentant*

8. **collaborate** (kə lab´ ə rāt) *v.* to work with another toward a goal
   The lyricist and composer *collaborated* on the stage musical.
   syn: cooperate

9. **impound** (im pownd´) *v.* to confine; to retain in legal custody
   The police *impounded* Dave's car after they found traces of cocaine on the upholstery.
   syn: confiscate   *ant: release*

10. **impeccable** (im pek´ ə bəl) *adj.* faultless; without sin or blemish
    Karl's appearance was *impeccable*, from his polished shoes to his neatly combed hair.
    syn: immaculate; faultless; irreproachable   *ant: fallible; blameworthy*

11. **inane** (in ān´) *adj.* without sense or meaning; silly
    Still dazed from the head injury, Catherine made only *inane* comments.
    syn: foolish; insipid   *ant: significant; meaningful*

12. **expatriate** (eks pā´ trē ət) *n.* someone who chooses to live outside of, or renounce,
    his or her native country
    Although T. S. Eliot was born in America, he was an *expatriate* for most of his life and
    is often considered British.

13. **frowzy** (frow´ zē) *adj.* unkempt
    The lady's *frowzy* hair was so tangled that it looked like Spanish moss.
    syn: slovenly   *ant: tidy*

14. **evoke** (i vōk´) *v.* to summon forth
    The comedian was unable to *evoke* much of a response from the crowd.
    syn: conjure up; elicit

15. **emulate** (em´ yə lāt) *v.* to strive to be equal to; to imitate
    Jonas *emulated* his older brother by pursuing a career in the military.
    syn: copy

Exercise I

Words in Context

From the list below, supply the words needed to complete the paragraph. Some words will not be used.

magnanimous   impeccable   ~~impound~~   ~~contrite~~
expatriate   ~~emulate~~   ~~collaborate~~

1. "Don't _____ me, kid—unless you want to spend time in the slammer, too," Buddy laughed as he put his hands in the air and glanced around. "But if you're really interested, maybe we can *collaborate* on 'helping' you pick the winning horse."

   Lucas didn't return his uncle's smirk, and Buddy became *contrite*. Lucas never really adapted to conversing through a sheet of Plexiglas, and the tinny sound of Buddy's musing through the two-way intercom made him uncomfortable. Lucas came to the prison only because the police were going to *impound* Buddy's car if no one removed it from the credit union parking lot, and Lucas thought that he was being _____ by mentioning that he, like Buddy, had an interest in horse racing.

From the list below, supply the words needed to complete the paragraph. Some words will not be used.

evoke   ~~expatriate~~   heinous   frowzy
inane   ~~sere~~   ~~enhance~~   postulate

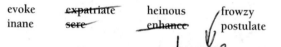

2. Jerry squinted and ran his hand through his *frowzy* mop of hair. The Pacific sun was already high in the sky, and he had a lot of work to accomplish before his guests arrived that evening. Originally from a Minnesota dairy, Jerry had lived on the tiny Micronesian island for over sixteen years. He never really considered himself to be a[n] *expatriate*, but then again, he didn't plan to return to the United States, either. Thinking that it might be a good idea to *enhance* his front yard before his visitors arrived, Jerry grabbed a machete and walked to the coconut grove in front of his shack. Huffing, Jerry chopped at the *sere*, withered fronds hanging against the trunks of the palm trees. When he finished cutting the fronds, he gathered the stray coconuts—some months old—and piled them in the corner of his yard. The yard looked sharp, even with Jerry's dilapidated shack in the background. As a bonus, Jerry decided to place two rows of tiki-torches along the path to the shack. Jerry thought that such trinkets were *inane*, but he wanted his two nieces from Cleveland to get the total island experience.

From the list below, supply the words needed to complete the paragraph. Some words will not be used.

postulate   **evoke**   **expatriate**   **unctuous**
heinous   **impeccable**

3.   Jordan sat at the helm and surveyed the broken radio before speaking to Candace.
     "This is not going to be easy. You're going to have to _____ all the strength you have in order to succeed."
     In her typical sarcastic manner, Candace responded to Jordan in a[n] _____ tone. "Oh, really? Thank goodness you told me; I had _____ that swimming two miles through an oil slick would be easy!"
     Candace walked over to the porthole and looked at the horizon. The line where the earth met the sky was tilted by at least seven or eight degrees; the *Nittany* was definitely taking on water. The wounded tanker in the distance wasn't doing much better; from the *Nittany*'s bridge, Jordan could tell where the tanker's hull had ruptured by a black swirl slowly meandering through the crystal clear water.
     "Do you remember what you're doing?"
     "Piece of cake," said Jordan. "Be sure to give him the proper coordinates; I'm not going down with the ship."
     "Oh, don't worry," snapped Candace. "Any shark that eats you will immediately spit you back out."
     "Ha-ha. Thanks for the _____ image of my certain death."
     "Oh, relax. Once we get out of this, I'll treat you to a[n] _____ lobster dinner on Maui. See ya later!" With that, Candace walked out of the bridge and jumped over the handrail. Jordan didn't even hear the splash.

Exercise II

Sentence Completion

Complete the sentence in a way that shows you understand the meaning of the italicized vocabulary word.

1.   Some people try to *enhance* their looks by… using makup

2.   The bandit's *heinous* record included the crimes of… Several People

3.   The *sere* peach tree finally collapsed because… it didn't have water

4.   Known to be a shrine of *impeccable* art, Marlene's home was filled with… Art

5.   The *contrite* thief apologized for… Stealing the Art

6.   The *expatriate* writer decided never to return to… France

7.   In his typical *magnanimous* manner, Richard ignored his sister's habitual… Singing.

8. Police *impounded* Shauna's car because she… *double Parked it*

9. Your *inane* behavior is not acceptable during… *class*

10. The old medium attempted to *evoke* the spirit of… *God*

11. The *frowzy* old man had obviously been living… *in Garbage*

12. Maggie *emulates* her older sister by… *Stealing here cloths*

13. If you *postulate* outcomes based on old research, then you risk… *dieing*

14. Expect an *unctuous* greeting from the maitre d' if you… *are rude*

15. The Army and the Air Force must *collaborate* during… *WW III*

Exercise III

Roots, Prefixes, and Suffixes

Study the entries and answer the questions that follow.

The root *cogn* means "know" or "think."
The root *carn* means "flesh."
The root *vor* means "eat."
The prefix *in–* means "not." (It can also mean "in.")
The prefix *re–* means "again."

1. Using *literal* translations as guidance, define the following words without using a dictionary:

      A. incognito   D. carnivore
      B. cogitation   E. carnivorous
      C. cognizant   F. reincarnate

2. In the Latin phrase "*cogito ergo sum*," *ergo* means "therefore," and *sum* means "I am." What do you suppose the entire phrase means?

3. A carnival used to refer specifically to a holiday or holidays that took place just before the start of Lent. Since Lent was a time when eating meat was forbidden, what do you suppose *carnival* meant?

4. List as many words as you can think of that contain the forms *cogn* or *carn*.

Exercise IV

Inference

Complete the sentence by inferring information about the italicized word from its context.

1. Kayla wants to *enhance* the appearance of her room, so she should...

2. Dalton's older brother is a fireman, and Dalton used to *emulate* him by...

3. The *expatriate* never visits her native country, and she often talks about...

Exercise V

Writing

Here is a writing prompt similar to the one you will find on the writing portion of an assessment test.

Plan and write an essay based on the following statement:

> Some men see things as they are and say "Why?" I dream things that never were and say, "Why not?"
>
> –George Bernard Shaw
> *Back to Methuselah* (1921)

Assignment: Write an essay in which you explain George Bernard Shaw's quotation. What is implied in contrasting the two types of people? Be certain to illustrate and support all of your points with examples and evidence from your own reading, classroom studies, and personal observation and experience.

Thesis: Write a *one-sentence* response to the above assignment. Make certain this single sentence offers a clear statement of your position.

Example: George Bernard Shaw's quotation describes the difference between those people who understand and those who create, and both are necessary in the world.

_____

_____

Organizational Plan: List at least three subtopics you will use to support your main idea. This list is your outline.

1. _____

2. _____

3. _____

Draft: Following your outline, write a good first draft of your essay. Remember to support all your points with examples, facts, references to reading, etc.

Review and Revise: Exchange essays with a classmate. Using the Holistic scoring guide on page 262, score your partner's essay (while he or she scores yours). If necessary, rewrite your essay to correct the problems noted by your partner.

Exercise VI

English Practice

Identifying Sentence Errors

Identify the grammatical error in each of the following sentences. If the sentence contains no error, select answer choice E.

1. High levels of air pollution causes damage to the respiratory tract.   No error
   (A)   (B)   (C)   (D)   (E)

2. Sally and Jane goes to the mall every day.   No error
   (A)   (B)   (C)   (D)   (E)

3. Each flower, tree, shrub, and bush need watering.   No error
   (A)   (B)   (C)   (D)   (E)

4. A young couple was strolling through the park while holding hands.   No error
   (A)   (B)   (C)   (D)   (E)

5. The number of volunteers for the military is declining.   No error
   (A)   (B)   (C)   (D)   (E)

Improving Sentences

The underlined portion of each sentence below contains some flaw. Select the answer choice that best corrects the flaw.

6. John was not only a talented student but also was a great athlete.
   A.   not only a talented student, but also a great athlete.
   B.   only a talented student, but also was a great athlete.
   C.   not only a talented student, but also was great.
   D.   not only a talented student, but was also a great athlete.
   E.   a talented student, a great athlete.

7. My niece could not be <u>persuaded that giving is as much a joy as receiving</u>.
    A. persuaded that giving is as much a joy as to receive.
    B. persuaded that to give is as much a joy as receiving.
    C. convinced that giving is as much a joy as to receive.
    D. made to feel that giving is as much a joy as to receive.
    E. No revision needed.

8. Our leaders <u>believe and live by the law</u>.
    A. trust and live by the law.
    B. believe in and live by the law.
    C. believe in and live the law.
    D. obey in and live by the law.
    E. trust and obey by the law.

9. <u>The earth is bluer than any planet in our solar system</u>.
    A. The earth is bluer than any planets in our solar system.
    B. The earth is bluer than a planet in our system.
    C. The earth is bluer than any other planet in our solar system.
    D. The earth is bluer than any planet in the solar system.
    E. No revision needed.

10. <u>The person who expects the worst frequently has the worst happen.</u>
    A. The person, who expects the worst frequently, has the worst happen.
    B   The person, who expects the worst, frequently has the worst happen.
    C. The person who expects the worst frequently, has the worst happen.
    D. The person who expects the worst, frequently, has the worst happen.
    E. No revision required.

Review Lessons 7-9

Exercise I

Inferences

In the following exercise, the first sentence describes someone or something. Infer information from the first sentence, and then choose the word from the Word Bank that best completes the second sentence.

sardonic	impounded	austere	droll
emulated	decorum	collaborated	ambivalent

1. Maddy was not sure how to feel about the illegal immigration policy because, while her own parents were immigrants, it had taken them years of struggling and persistent effort to become citizens legally.

    From this sentence, we can infer that Maddy is _____ about the subject of immigration.

2. When out on the range for weeks at a time, the cowboy sleeps in a 4-by-8-foot shack, cooks over an open fire, and works every day, no matter what the weather is like.

    From this sentence, we can infer that the cowboy works in _____ conditions.

3. After Jacob read a biography on Teddy Roosevelt, he began to dress and speak like his hero.

    From this sentence, we can infer that Jacob _____ Teddy Roosevelt.

4. Because no single nation had all the resources to build the orbiting solar power station on its own, several nations worked together for many years to plan and build the massive project.

    From this sentence, we can infer that the nations _____ on the space station.

5. The boy who had been raised by wolves was still prone to walk around on all fours when nervous, and he never used silverware when he ate.

    From this sentence, we can infer that the boy never had a chance to develop a sense of proper _____ when interacting with people.

Exercise II

Related Words

Some of the vocabulary words from Lessons 7 through 9 have related meanings. Complete the following sentences by choosing the word that best fits the context, based on information you infer from the use of the italicized word. Some word pairs will be antonyms, some will be synonyms, and some will simply be words often used in the same context.

1. The senior officers _____ that the assault strategy was *inane* and should be changed immediately or the battle would certainly be lost.
   A. concurred
   B. transposed
   C. propagated
   D. abated
   E. emulated

2. The sheik's _____ desert lodging and toilsome lifestyle *belied* his immense wealth, known only to his tribe and his family.
   A. sardonic
   B. ambivalent
   C. contrite
   D. inane
   E. austere

3. Unwilling to be fooled by the *demagogue's* patriotic speeches any longer, hordes of angry citizens created a[n] _____ of the ruler and burned it in the palace courtyard.
   A. journeyman
   B. dilemma
   C. culmination
   D. effigy
   E. intern

4. When asked a difficult question about a pending ecological disaster, the *erudite* professor offered such a[n] _____ and thorough solution that it sounded as though it had been rehearsed.
   A. ambivalent
   B. sardonic
   C. glib
   D. contrite
   E. heinous

5. Rather than counting on the donations of _____ strangers, the *destitute* family worked twice as hard as anyone until they had saved enough to get back on their feet.
    A.   inane
    B.   heinous
    C.   expatriate
    D.   magnanimous
    E.   austere

6. The explorers feared that a wrong word or hand gesture might be a[n] _____ to their hosts, a native tribe whose feast *decorum* was unknown to all outsiders.
    A.   duplicity
    B.   affront
    C.   effigy
    D.   dilemma
    E.   demagogue

7. The *duplicity* of the con artist's crimes made them especially _____, because the criminal had stolen the life savings of people who had been his close friends for many years.
    A.   intrepid
    B.   destitute
    C.   austere
    D.   magnanimous
    E.   heinous

8. Still _____ for having been harsh with the children, the *demure* father spoke very little during dinner.
    A.   impeccable
    B.   contrite
    C.   inane
    D.   unctuous
    E.   sardonic

9. The *intern* at the research laboratory chose a mentor whom she could _____ as she learned the systems and procedures the seasoned professional used.
    A.   concur
    B.   transpose
    C.   enhance
    D.   emulate
    E.   abhor

10. An underwater volcano _____ the tsunami wave across miles of open ocean, but the wave *abated* in the shallows, where it lost energy to the sea floor.
    A.   propagated
    B.   collaborated
    C.   postulated
    D.   abhorred
    E.   transposed

Exercise III

Deeper Meanings

Choose a word to replace the italicized word in each sentence. All of the possible choices for each sentence have similar definitions, but the correct answer will have a connotation that best suits the context. For example, the words "delete," "destroy," and "obliterate" all mean "to remove or wipe out," but no one would ever say, "I destroyed the name from the document." The correct choice will be the word that has the best specific meaning and does not render the sentence awkward in tone or content. When choices seem close, look for a clue in the context that makes one choice better than the other.

Note that the correct answer is not always the primary vocabulary word from the lesson.

confused	erudite	destitute	dumb	freezing
austere	inane	slovenly	inhospitable	
poor	hard	unkempt	educated	

1. The banker lost not just his opulent mansion and cars, but all of his friends, too, leaving him truly *broke* and sleeping on park benches.

    Better word: _____

2. Though the lady's maid had grown up in poverty, her *smart* speech and vast knowledge revealed that she had received a superior education.

    Better word: _____

3. After her plane crashed in the remote Yukon, Darma endured *difficult* conditions, without supplies, for three weeks before rescuers located her.

    Better word: _____

4. After showing up at a job interview while wearing sweatpants, sandals, and a t-shirt spotted with potato chip grease, the *frowzy* man wondered why he didn't get a job offer.

    Better word: _____

5. To show off, the jet pilot buzzed the control tower, missing it by mere yards, and was consequently arrested and dishonorably discharged for putting lives in danger with his *silly* actions.

    Better word: _____

Exercise IV

Crossword Puzzle

Use the clues to complete the crossword puzzle. The answers consist of vocabulary words from Lessons 7 through 9.

Across

1. copycat
6. like a thief who got caught
10. way too nice
12. on the streets
15. big dummy
16. not sure what to think
17. said way too easily
18. not afraid of anything

Down

2. anti-hermit
3. lock up
4. agree
5. like hard times
7. like someone you want on your trivia team
8. work with a buddy
9. a butcher, baker, or candlestick maker
11. person likely to pound fist during speech
13. give the wrong impression
14. like a raisin in the sun

Exercise V

Subject Prompts

Here is a writing prompt similar to the one you will find on the writing portion of an assessment test. Follow the instructions below and write a brief, efficient essay.

> It is no secret that the United States, among all nations of the free world, is one of the least enthusiastic about teaching and learning foreign languages, even amid new heights in global economies and the rise of international communication through literature, films, and the Internet.
>
> How important is it, if at all, to learn a foreign language? Many schools require two to four years of foreign language study, but often that is not enough to foster fluency. Should schools mandate foreign language fluency? Write a letter to the Secretary of Education that outlines your argument. Support your stance with at least three reasons explaining why you think foreign language fluency should or should not be a priority in primary and secondary education. Your motive in writing the letter, for the purpose of this exercise, is to either appropriate or spare millions of dollars in Federal funds—tax dollars—for a nationwide program.

Thesis: Write a *one-sentence* response to the above assignment. Make certain this single sentence offers a clear statement of your position.

Example: While the merits of learning more than one language are unquestionable, they are not worth purchasing for the price of national debt.

_____

_____

Organizational Plan: List at least three subtopics you will use to support your main idea. This list is your outline.

1. _____

2. _____

3. _____

Draft: Following your outline, write a good first draft of your essay. Remember to support all your points with examples, facts, references to reading, etc.

Review and Revise: Exchange essays with a classmate. Using the scoring guide for Sentence Formation and Variety on page 260, score your partner's essay (while he or she scores yours). Focus on sentence structure and the use of language conventions. If necessary, rewrite your essay to improve the sentence structure and/or your use of language.

Lesson Ten

1. **cajole** (kə jōl´) *v.* to persuade with false promises and flattery
   Despite her best efforts, the mayor could not *cajole* Madame Harris into donating the land to the city.
   syn: coax; wheedle *ant: dissuade; deter*

2. **expound** (ik spownd´) *v.* to explain in detail; to clarify
   Closing the Bible, the minister *expounded* on the passage he had just read.
   syn: elaborate *ant: muddle; confuse*

3. **métier** (me tyā´) *n.* the work one is especially suited for; one's specialty; an occupation
   Justin is a decent singer, but dancing is his real *métier*.
   syn: forte *ant: weakness*

4. **balk** (bôk) *v.* to refuse stubbornly or abruptly; to stop short and refuse to go on
   Although Paul desperately needed the money, he *balked* at the idea of working for less than minimum wage.
   syn: hesitate; object *ant: agree; continue*

5. **incognito** (in kog nē´ tō) *adj.* disguised; pretending not to be oneself
   To avoid clamoring fans, the actor donned a disguise and traveled *incognito*.

6. **acrimony** (a´ krə mō nē) *n.* ill-natured, bitter hostility
   Because of his *acrimony*, the old man found himself lonely and friendless.
   syn: animosity *ant: friendliness*

7. **dour** (dowr) *adj.* stern and ill-humored
   The librarian's *dour* expression and stereotypical bifocals contradicted her tattoos and noisy motorcycle.
   syn: forbidding *ant: pleasant*

8. **harry** (har´ ē) *v.* to annoy or harass
   The baby's constant crying began to *harry* the other passengers on the train.
   syn: bother; pester *ant: soothe*

9. **omniscient** (om nish´ ənt) *adj.* having unlimited knowledge; all-knowing
   Dad described Santa Claus as an *omniscient* old man who knew whether we had been bad or good this year.

10. **feasible** (fē´ zə bəl) *adj.* reasonable; capable of being carried out
    Though he is still young, Jeff has a *feasible* plan to participate in the Olympic games.
    syn: possible; doable   *ant: unworkable*

11. **fiasco** (fē as´ kō) *n.* a complete, ridiculous failure
    Our first date was a *fiasco*: I lost a contact lens, we got mugged, and a child threw up on Amber's shoes in the subway.
    syn: disaster   *ant: success*

12. **inscrutable** (in skrōō´ tə bəl) *adj.* not easily understood; hard to fathom
    The crazed stalker left an *inscrutable* message on my answering machine.
    syn: enigmatic   *ant: obvious; evident*

13. **fluctuate** (fluk´ chōō āt) *v.* to rise and fall; to vary irregularly
    The stock market *fluctuates* so much that it seems silly to get upset when your stock goes down; it will probably go back up tomorrow.
    syn: waver; vacillate   *ant: stabilize*

14. **lethargy** (leth´ ər jē) *n.* lack of energy; sluggishness
    The heat and humidity made me sink into the couch, too overwhelmed with *lethargy* to move.
    syn: torpor; lassitude   *ant: vigor; vitality*

15. **exult** (ig zult´) *v.* to rejoice; to feel triumphant
    When the results were announced, the town wildly *exulted* in its team's victory.
    syn: celebrate

Exercise I

Words in Context

From the list below, supply the words needed to complete the paragraph. Some words will not be used.

fluctuate	cajole	expound	acrimony
exult	inscrutable	métier	harry

1. Councilwoman Moore stepped up to the podium. "I don't think I need to _____ upon reasons for voting against the proposed construction; I thought that the message was clear enough at the last meeting—when you all opposed it as well. Obviously, someone has _____ a few of you into changing your opinion since last month, and your sudden, _____ decision to yield to Beta-Rad Enterprises bothers me a great deal. What happened to the surplus of _____ toward Beta-Rad from the last meeting? Don't you remember how we _____ in our victory over the radioactive waste dump? For two years, we've listened to Beta-Rad executives _____ us, and we finally had the chance to stop it for good. How could the opinions of fifteen people possibly _____ this much?"

From the list below, supply the words needed to complete the paragraph. Some words will not be used.

incognito	feasible	dour	fiasco	métier
lethargy	balk	omniscient	harry	

2. "Hey, Jye; I think you've found your _____."
    "Could be." Jye glanced up only long enough to catch a glimpse of Neve. Typing rapidly, Jye intermittently glanced at the stack of printed matrixes next to the keyboard. Usually a[n] _____ person who remained hidden in his software-engineer cubicle all day, Jye adopted a manner bordering on cynicism and _____—getting him to do tech support beyond his cubicle walls was often a[n] _____ that created more trouble than it solved. Neve was caught completely off-guard when Jye didn't _____ at the company's request that he test the system's network security by hacking into the company database. Though Jye had his ways, everyone knew that he was the _____ office authority when it came to network security protocol. It simply wouldn't have been _____ to use anyone else to test the integrity of Pentacode's newest software. Additionally, Jye's newfound energy changed his manner so much that he might as well have been _____ to those who didn't see him every day; when his attitude changed, his wardrobe and hairstyle changed as well.

Exercise II

Sentence Completion

Complete the sentence in a way that shows you understand the meaning of the italicized vocabulary word.

1. Milton's *fluctuating* condition prevents the doctor from...

2. Ann's *lethargy* was not due to the heat; she was simply...

3. The wedding went well, but the *acrimony* between the families resulted in...

4. Please *expound* on your explanation of...

5. The *inscrutable* actions of the building inspector caused...

6. The monkeys, native to India, sometimes *harry* villagers by...

7. To avoid a *fiasco* during your camping trip, be sure to...

8. I would have donated money, but I *balked* when I learned that...

9. A *feasible* reason for missing work would be...

10. If the warden were indeed *omniscient*, then he would know that...

11. Finally able to dismount from his bicycle, Lance did not *exult* despite...

12. Uncle Tony was not originally a *dour* man; ten years ago, he...

13. Caitlyn, a remarkable writer, found her *métier* as...

14. Not even six years of *cajoling* could convince Mrs. Garcia to...

15. Wary of being discovered by the rebels, the *incognito* Colonel Lito...

Exercise III

Roots, Prefixes, and Suffixes

Study the entries and answer the questions that follow.

The root *agri* means "field" or "farming."
The suffixes *–ous* and *–ose* mean "full of."
The root *bell* means "war."
The root *gere* means "bearing" or "waging."
The prefix *ante–* means "before."
The suffix *–onomy* means "study of."

1. Using *literal* translations as guidance, define the following words without using a dictionary:

   A. antebellum   D. belligerent
   B. bellicose   E. anteroom
   C. agriculture   F. agronomy

2. The roots *ces* and *ced* mean "to go"; therefore, an *antecedent* is a word that

   _____.

3. An industrial society is characterized by cities and manufacturing; an *agrarian* society is characterized by _____.

4. List as many words as you can think of that contain the forms *agr* or *ante–*.

Exercise IV

Inference

Complete the sentences by inferring information about the italicized word from its context.

1. If an *avid* skier crashes on the slope, you can assume that…

2. If you *harry* the stray dog, it's quite possible that it will…

3. Mom must have been *omniscient* if she knew that Derek secretly…

Exercise V

Critical Reading

Below is a reading passage followed by several multiple-choice questions. Carefully read the passage and choose the best answer for each of the questions.

The author of this passage writes about the Victorian Era (1837–1901) in Great Britain.

Despite its cruel working conditions and mass poverty, Victorian England will always be remembered as a forerunner to the modern industrial society. As an incubator for early industry, 19th-century England was the first dominion in the world to experience the cultural byproducts that accompanied advancements in transportation and technology. The resulting cultural shifts
5   spawned a bouquet of unique historical attributes that today classify Victorian England.

Railways—the new method of mass land transportation to meet the blooming demands of early mass production—were at the heart of Victorian England's changes. Stimulating industry, railroads inspired advancements in coal mining, iron production, and construction engineering that resulted in better buildings, bridges, and machines. These advancements, in turn, made England
10   the foremost machine manufacturer in the world.

As the demand for industry increased, so did the demand for a working class: skilled artisans, craftsmen, and domestic outworkers who didn't necessitate the construction of more facilities. The boom in skilled workers—and their money—created a demand for more middle-class members such as doctors, bankers, and lawyers. Manufacturing also caused growth in the middle class
15   due to requirements for educated professionals such as architects, engineers, and entrepreneurs.

The growth and importance of the new working class caused many of the British to **balk** at the existing class structure in which the upper class appeared to reap the most benefits without having to endure the subhuman conditions of early factories. Realizing that they were crucial to industry, workers demonstrated their importance by organizing strikes in an effort to obtain better wages
20   and working conditions. Forerunners of this movement were the Chartists, who not only wanted to enhance working conditions, but also to redesign the government of England. The Chartists failed to change Parliament, but they did succeed in persuading Parliament to pass several acts from 1833 to 1847 that created more **feasible** working conditions for women and children.

The literature of England reflected the new social consciousness of the Victorian period. Mass
25   manufacturing led to cheap publishing, making books available for the increasingly literate masses, regardless of economic class. Owing to the availability of books, novels became popular, and the prevalent subjects of literature changed. In a departure from Romantic literature, fiction entertained contemporary affairs and aspects of common living instead of ancient legends and kingly heroes. Writers such as Lewis Carroll and Charles Dickens were free to satirize the estab-
30   lishment or to **expound** on the austere lives that many of the working class endured every day.

New schools of thought also emerged because of the new, convenient way to distribute information, often to the benefit of the working class. Activists such as the Chartists explored new or better forms of government, drawing ideas from people and events throughout the world, one of whom was Karl Marx. In 1840, Karl Marx wrote the Communist Manifesto while workers were at
35   the depths of misery. Marx's ideas favored the strength of the workers rather than the ingenuity of industry leaders, which immediately became an inspiration to many deprived workers. Although it preceded the era by a generation, the American War of independence also fueled **acrimony** between the classes in Victorian England, especially now that the middle class could read about the exploits of American Revolutionary leaders and their ideas about human equality and inherent
40   rights. Penny magazines, cheap to produce and easy to distribute, helped inflame the passions of the working class. New philosophies emerged, as well, some of which exemplified the legitimacy of science. Charles Darwin's *The Origin of Species*, published in 1859, caused traditional modes of thought to **fluctuate**; some people embraced Positivism, which states that concrete evidence and scientific laws govern the universe, and that sensory observation, or empirical evidence, is the

45   foundation of all valid knowledge, as opposed to guesses.

     The changing perspectives of Victorian England also inspired artists and architects to depart from traditional styles. Designers abandoned classical décor for Gothic spires or gaudy embellishments and stained glass windows, creating unique designs that, to this day, many people easily identify as Victorian. Like the dividing social classes, artists also held to different opinions
50   about the role of art. Some artists, threatened by the growth of industry, thought that art should remind people that they are human beings and not machines. Other Victorian artists debated over whether to maintain a classical style or to embrace realism. Like literature, new forms of art were in high demand owing to the growing middle-class audience.

     The railways of Victorian England carried much more than simple cargo and passengers; they
55   carried the sweeping changes that would blanket the world in a new era—the Industrial Age— and it would last more than 200 years, until factories and railways would slowly disintegrate as technology carried humans into the Age of Information. The remnants from the era will continue to stand, however, in the form of Gothic cathedrals, Queen Anne homes, and miles of steel bridges constructed in a time when human effort was meant to be timeless.

1A. The primary intent of this passage is to
    A.   explain the nineteenth century as it relates to technology.
    B.   discuss the impact of industry on culture worldwide.
    C.   offer a theory on the "Age of the Railway."
    D.   discuss the changes that occurred in Victorian England.
    E.   explain how the invention of the railroad influenced thought.

1B. Choose the topic that is not mentioned as having contributed to the evolution of Victorian England.
    A.   philosophy
    B.   art
    C.   social class
    D.   science
    E.   photography

2A. The style of this essay is best described as
    A.   informational.
    B.   descriptive.
    C.   humorous.
    D.   self-reflective.
    E.   speculative.

2B. Your answer to question 2A is best supported by
    A.   the absence of any noticeable personal opinions.
    B.   the use of slang and casual language.
    C.   the heavy discussion of science.
    D.   the many instances of imagery in the passage.
    E.   the author's use of the third-person point of view.

3A. As used in paragraph 3, the phrase "domestic outworkers" most likely means
    A. workers who do not show up to their jobs.
    B. factory workers who are not paid.
    C. people who work from their homes.
    D. people who work outside their homes.
    E. people who do housework for other people.

3B. What inference can logically be made from your answer to question 3A?
    A. Outworkers were the lowest class of workers and usually shunned.
    B. Railroads allowed outworkers to travel to jobs far from their homes.
    C. Technology allowed outworkers to organize strikes.
    D. Outworkers were hired to impede competing companies.
    E. Employers saved money by hiring outworkers.

4A. As used in line 27, the term "Romantic" most likely refers to
    A. the condition of being in love.
    B. the period immediately preceding the Victorian Era.
    C. the art and philosophy of ancient Rome.
    D. a Roman artist.
    E. a focus on poetry.

4B. Based on its description in the passage, Romantic literature would not typically have featured which one of the following subjects?
    A. ancient epics
    B. wartime sadness
    C. country farms
    D. powered machines
    E. natural elements

5A. According to lines 24-27, which of the following advances helped the novel to become popular?
    A. inexpensive publishing
    B. the Communists
    C. a growing population
    D. coal mining
    E. ink production techniques

5B. Which concurrent Victorian England advancement directly contributed to your answer to question 5A?
    A. a new middle class
    B. growing literacy
    C. an increasing upper class
    D. new tastes in literature
    E. the appearance of labor activists

6A. According to the passage, which element of Victorian England was the catalyst for most of the advances?
   A.   Positivism
   B.   Gothic architecture
   C.   factories
   D.   railroads
   E.   the American Revolution

6B. In the context of this passage, which of the following is *not* one of the advancements that would have been based on the correct answer to 6A?
   A.   iron production
   B.   coal mining
   C.   automobile manufacturing
   D.   construction engineering
   E.   better bridges

7A. As used in line 43, "Positivism" is most likely the belief that
   A.   electrical charges are responsible for life.
   B.   optimistic people will attract others like them.
   C.   experience is the only basis for knowledge.
   D.   nature always balances itself.
   E.   only the good survive changes.

7B. To successfully gather empirical evidence during an experiment, a scientist would need to
   A.   form a guess as to the outcome of the experiment.
   B.   take precise measurements during the experiment.
   C.   conclude how he or she thinks the experiment will run.
   D.   propose a theory to explain any phenomena that is not understood.
   E.   read reports about similar experiments.

8. The author of the passage ascribes the increased demand for art to which aspect of Victorian England?
   A.   the shrinking working class
   B.   the diminishing middle class
   C.   the growing working class
   D.   the growing middle class
   E.   the new ideas in Parliament

9A. This passage would most likely be found in
   A.   a literature blog.
   B.   an encyclopedia of politics.
   C.   a British history book.
   D.   an American history book.
   E.   a book on architecture.

9B. Choose the most suitable title for the passage.
A. Advancement in Victorian England
B. A Change in Ideas
C. How Art and Literature Changed England
D. Communism in England
E. Political Change in Victorian England

10. Which choice best describes the implication of the following line?

"The remnants from the era will continue to stand, however, in the form of Gothic cathedrals, Queen Anne homes, and miles of steel bridges constructed in a time when human effort was meant to be timeless."

A. People of the Victorian age did not want to influence future generations.
B. Steel was cheap in Victorian England, and architects were plentiful.
C. Craftsmanship was better a century ago than it is in the present.
D. The proof of the advancements of Victorian England have been lost with time.
E. Victorian building practices resulted in crowded construction of cities.

Lesson Eleven

1. **harangue** (hə rang´) *n.* a long, strongly expressed speech or lecture
My wife delivered a lengthy *harangue* this morning in an effort to get me to quit smoking.
syn: tirade

2. **grandiloquent** (gran dil´ ə kwent) *adj.* pompous or high-flown in speech
Marcus gets *grandiloquent* when speaking of the theatre, assuming no one knows as much or has as refined a taste as he.
syn: pretentious   *ant: plain-spoken*

3. **avid** (av´ id) *adj.* enthusiastic; extremely interested
Dori was such an *avid* reader that I had a hard time recommending a title she had not yet read.
syn: voracious; eager   *ant: apathetic*

4. **epistle** (i pis´ əl) *n.* a letter or literary composition in letter form
Brian spent years writing lengthy, unsent *epistles* to his old girlfriend.

5. **humility** (hyōō mil´ i tē) *n.* absence of vanity; humbleness
Even though Jo is a celebrated author, she's the picture of *humility* and never brags.
syn: modesty   *ant: vanity; arrogance*

6. **dolorous** (dō´ lə rəs) *adj.* exhibiting sorrow or pain
The song was so *dolorous* that Laura found it difficult not to cry.
syn: mournful   *ant: joyous*

7. **explicit** (ik splis´ it) *adj.* clearly and openly stated; leaving nothing to the imagination
Mom's instructions were *explicit*: Do not leave the house for any reason.
syn: exact; precise   *ant: ambiguous; vague*

8. **gargantuan** (gär gan´ chōō ən) *adj.* of huge or extraordinary size and power
Milltown's players were *gargantuan* compared with the small guys on our team.
syn: gigantic; huge   *ant: tiny*

9. **gadfly** (gad´ flī) *n.* an irritating and persistent person
I tried to lose Judy, an obnoxious *gadfly*, in the crowd, but she stuck to me with unbearable closeness.
syn: nuisance; pest

10. **arduous** (är´ jōō əs) *adj.* difficult; requiring much effort
Refinishing the old bookcase proved an *arduous* task, but the results were well worth it.
syn: strenuous; laborious   *ant: easy; unchallenging*

11. **affable** (af´ ə bel) *adj.* friendly; agreeable; easy to talk to
The *affable* old man never lacked for visitors.
syn: amiable; good-natured   *ant: disagreeable; irascible*

12. **agrarian** (ə grâr´ ē ən) *adj.* concerning farms, farmers, or the use of land
The economy of the *agrarian* nation depended on good crop yields.
syn: agricultural   *ant: urban; industrial*

13. **formidable** (fôr´ mi də bəl) *adj.* arousing fear or awe
When the hulking, 250-lb man stepped into the ring, Oscar knew that he was facing a *formidable* opponent.
syn: intimidating

14. **sycophant** (sik´ ə fənt) *n.* a flatterer; one who fawns on others in order to gain favor
Teri was such a *sycophant* that she always laughed loudly at her supervisor's awful jokes.
syn: toady   *ant: contrarian*

15. **grimace** (grim´ is) *n.* a facial expression of fear, disapproval, or pain
Amanda gave a *grimace* when Mrs. Hind assigned nine pages of algebra homework.
syn: scowl   *ant: smile*

Exercise I

Words in Context

From the list below, supply the words needed to complete the paragraph. Some words will not be used.

gadfly	humility	arduous	affable	grandiloquent
harangue	grimace	sycophant	explicit	agrarian

1. "All the king's horses and all the king's men showed up tonight!" mused Wyston to himself as he snatched another glass of champagne from the server's tray. He hated the governor's cocktail parties; it was always a[n] _____ task to maintain a friendly, _____ demeanor around so many obvious _____ seeking favors from the administration. After two hours, Wyston had to struggle to prevent his tired, polite smile from turning into a _____. It took all he had to pretend to listen and nod at the _____ stories of the "wannabe rich and famous." There was also the annoying babble of the _____—single attendees who lacked the _____ required to be seen alone. They forced themselves into conversations and then held the listeners captive by withholding any opportunities to escape. When Wyston could no longer tolerate the pestering, he stepped outside and waited for the Governor to arrive and deliver his _____ to the idiotic crowd.

From the list below, supply the words needed to complete the paragraph. Some words will not be used.

humility	dolorous	agrarian	gadfly	gargantuan
avid	explicit	formidable	epistle	

2. The atmosphere at Aunt Agnes's farmhouse was _____ during the wake following the funeral. No one could believe that Agnes was gone. At least, they reasoned, the _____ equestrian died while doing something that she loved. There was no definite explanation as to why Agnes's horse had bucked her off, but by the looks of the _____ animal tracks, the horse had been spooked by a[n] _____ wolf, perhaps the largest ever seen.

    The threat of wolves was nothing new to the _____ Van Ness family, who had been farming the northern valley for six generations. Wolves had attacked horses on the farm in the past, especially during extremely cold winters such as this one. Children on the farm always had _____ instructions to stay within sight of the house, but sometimes not even that was enough to protect the family from the hungry, silver predators.

    Vicky, a niece, wandered up the stairway to the second floor. Memories of her youth flashed through her head as she entered Agnes's room, sat on the corner of the bed, and noticed the dusty corner of an old shoebox protruding from beneath the vanity. Curious, Vicky retrieved the box and, to her surprise, she found thirty years of hand-written _____, some of which were for Agnes, and some of which Agnes wrote but never sent.

Exercise II

Sentence Completion

Complete the sentence in a way that shows you understand the meaning of the italicized vocabulary word.

1. The history teacher's *harangue* this morning seemed to...

2. Through the smoke, I could tell by the *grimace* on Danforth's face that he...

3. The *affable* receptionist made everyone feel...

4. To the dismay of the *sycophants*, the new foreman...

5. Jamie, the annoying *gadfly*, has a habit of...

6. The beach town published *explicit* rules about...

7. The summer help on the highway crew underestimated the *arduous* task of...

8. The arrogant stockbroker learned *humility* after...

9. In *agrarian* states, many young adults have extensive knowledge of...

10. Needing a break from her *dolorous* work as a coroner, Dr. Sinclair...

11. Unlike the fox, the bear turned out to be a *formidable* opponent because...

12. Elliot could hardly tolerate the *grandiloquent* aristocrats while working at the...

13. Mary Ellen's *avid* interest in chemistry led to her career as...

14. The senator's biography was actually a collection of *epistles* that...

15. The *gargantuan* Kodiak bear devoured...

Exercise III

Roots, Prefixes, and Suffixes

Study the entries and answer the questions that follow.

The root *cosm* means "world" or "universe."
The root *cred* means "believe."
The suffixes –*ic* and –*id* mean "of" or "like."

1. Using *literal* translations as guidance, define the following words without using a dictionary:

      A. cosmic   D. creed
      B. cosmos   E. credentials
      C. credible   F. credence

2. *Micro* means "small"; therefore, the word *microcosm* refers to a[n] _____.

3. *Polites* means "citizen"; therefore, a *cosmopolitan* person is _____.

4. List as many words as you can think of that contain the root *cred*.

Exercise IV

Inference

Complete the sentences by inferring information about the italicized word from its context.

1. Everyone knew that Bonnie was a *sycophant* because whenever the governor entered the room, Bonnie would…

2. If Kevin is no longer *affable* after his meeting with the manager, we might assume that the manager…

3. After the hard tackle during the championship game, the coach saw the *grimace* on Todd's face and knew…

Exercise V

Writing

Here is a writing prompt similar to the one you will find on the writing portion of an assessment test.

Plan and write an essay based on the following statement:

> If there were in the world today any large number of people who desired their own happiness more than they desired the unhappiness of others, we could have paradise in a few years.
>
> —Bertrand Russell

Assignment: After facing several student disciplinary problems related to the dress code, the administration of your school has decided to mandate school uniforms for students but not for the faculty. Using the quotation as your inspiration, express your opinion on the issue.

Thesis: Write a *one-sentence* response to the above assignment. Make certain this single sentence offers a clear statement of your position. The sentence should appear early in your first paragraph.

Example: The administration is subjecting the entire student body to unfair, discriminatory standards because it does not want to deal with a few problem students.

_____

_____

Organizational Plan: List at least three subtopics you will use to support your main idea. This list is your outline.

1. _____

2. _____

3. _____

Draft: Following your outline, write a good first draft of your essay. Remember to support all your points with examples, facts, references to reading, etc.

Review and Revise: Exchange essays with a classmate. Using the scoring guide for Organization on page 257, score your partner's essay (while he or she scores yours). Focus on the organizational plan and the use of language conventions. If necessary, rewrite your essay to improve the organizational plan and/or your use of language.

Exercise VI

Improving Paragraphs

Read the following passage and then answer the multiple-choice questions that follow. The questions will require you to make decisions regarding the revision of the reading selection.

1   On November 8, 1942, American soldiers landed in North Africa. Fighting alongside the British Eighth Army, the Allies pushed the Germans out of North Africa. When the **arduous** campaign was over, on May 12, 1943, the Allies had lost 70,000 men, while killing, wounding and capturing 350,000 Italian and German (Axis) soldiers. With North Africa taken, the Allies then invaded Italy. The plan was to drive up the boot of Italy, right into Germany, or so it seemed. Meanwhile, however, Allied plans were moving ahead toward the invasion of Europe on the French coast.

2   The German generals, pessimistic at this point in the war, had good reason to be. They were pressed on the Eastern front by the Russians and in Italy by the Allies. Additionally, the German generals had an entire continent on which a third battlefront would surely be opened. Hitler and his generals knew that the pending Allied invasion would have to be crushed quickly. Only in this way could Hitler send more men to halt the Russian advance in the East. It was in this mood Hitler named General Rommel to be in charge of coastal defenses in France. While Hitler blamed Rommel for the defeats in North Africa, he also knew that Rommel was the most brilliant general he had.

3   When Rommel arrived, he was amazed at how little defensive work had been done. Throwing himself into his work, Rommel began construction on what he called the Atlantic Wall. This was to be a wall of coastal defenses that stretched from Norway to Spain. If Rommel had had the benefit of a few more months, some observers think he might have affected the outcome of the invasion. Another problem was the confusion in the German general staff. Because no one on the scene had complete authority, important things frequently did not get done. If Rommel had been in complete charge, some experts think that the Allied invasion would have been in greater trouble.

4   On June 6, 1944, the invasion began. More than 150,000 Allied troops landed on the beaches. The **formidable** force landed on the northern coast of France at Normandy. Their mission was to push Hitler's army back across the continent and completely crush the Nazi war machine. The soldiers were mostly from Britain, Canada, and the United States. The landing force had been preceded by 13,000 paratroopers who dropped behind the enemy's lines. The total invasion force was backed by the full force of Allied sea and air power. In the air, the Allies enjoyed a fifty-to-one advantage. On the ground they conducted the biggest amphibious assault ever attempted in modern warfare. Equipment for this landing had been stockpiled in the south of England in the months before the invasion. Code named "Operation Overlord," it was more popularly known as "D-Day." This attack proved to be the beginning of the end for Hitler and Nazi Germany.

5   U.S. General Dwight Eisenhower was the Supreme Commander of Allied forces based in Britain. He had the responsibility for leading the attack on the European continent. Eisenhower had described the military power that waited for D-Day as "a coiled spring." It was his responsibility to pick the day on which "this coiled spring" would let loose. In other words he must make the decision on when to launch the attack. This was an awesome responsibility, and the bad weather in the Channel made it a tough decision. There had already been two delays because of the weather. On June 6, however, Eisenhower gave the signal for the invasion to begin. The timing could not have been better. A brief break in the rainy weather that day allowed the ships to land the men and the tanks. In addition, Field Marshall Rommel had been convinced that the gale-force winds would continue. Knowing that the Allies had a history of waiting for clear weather, Rommel decided that it was safe to return to Germany for his wife's birthday party. By the time he got back to the battlefront, the Allies were firmly dug in on French soil. The Allies had gotten a foothold on the continent, and they would not be turned back.

6 In planning the invasion, Eisenhower knew that fooling the enemy about the landing places was very important. In a brilliant plan of deception, Eisenhower had created a phony military unit called FUSAG or the First United States Army Group. Information was intentionally leaked to the Germans that this was the invading force that would land at Calais, France. Fake **epistles** were sent out and allowed to be intercepted, false troop locations were reported, and metal strips were dropped from planes to give the appearance of large air squadrons on German radar. This scheme was so convincing that Hitler was still waiting for the assault on Calais six weeks after the Allies landed at Normandy. The months following the assault on Normandy would see the Axis powers in full retreat on all fronts. It was too late for the Axis.

1. Which of the following would best improve the last two sentences of the first paragraph?
  A. Add, *it seemed,* after *plan,* put a semicolon after *Germany,* and delete *or so it seemed* and *Meanwhile.*
  B. Delete *however.*
  C. Delete *so it seemed* and combine the ideas into one sentence.
  D. Add *so it seemed* after *plan* and replace *Meanwhile, however,* with *But.*
  E. Delete both sentences.

2. How should paragraph 2 be edited to make it less confusing to the reader?
  A. Use *then* instead of *in this way,* delete *It was in this mood,* and capitalize *continent.*
  B. Delete the final paragraph.
  C. Replace *Only in this way* with *Only when crushed.*
  D. Delete the first sentence.
  E. Replace *Only in this way* with *Only by stopping the Allies,* place a semi-colon after *East,* and replace *It was in this mood* with *consequently.*

3. Paragraph 3 indicates *Another problem was the confusion.* Which of the following would best clarify what the initial problem was?
  A. Add a phrase to this sentence that begins, "the initial problem being...."
  B. Italicize the sentences that state the first problem.
  C. Explain again who General Rommel was.
  D. Delete the first sentence.
  E. Use the word *problem* earlier in the paragraph.

4. What should be done with the sentence in paragraph 5 that begins, *In other words* and ends with *attack?*
  A. Shorten it.
  B. Delete it.
  C. Lengthen it.
  D. Move it.
  E. Combine it with another sentence.

5. Which choice best describes a way to improve the last sentence of the passage?
  A. Rewrite it to refer to Germany instead of the Axis.
  B. Reemphasize the success of the FUSAG ruse.
  C. Delete the sentence.
  D. Use it as the topic sentence of a new concluding paragraph.
  E. Combine it with the sentence immediately before it.

Lesson Twelve

1. **lexicon** (lek´ si kon) *n.* a dictionary; a specialized vocabulary used in a
particular field or place
Having grown up in the inner city, Shawn was familiar with the *lexicon* of the streets.
syn: jargon; argot; cant

2. **hue** (hyōō) *n.* a particular shade of a given color
Dad was going to paint the shutters magenta, but Mom hates that *hue* and nixed the
idea.

3. **sanction** (sangk´ shən) *n.* permission; support
The teacher gave *sanction* to the student's odd but harmless habit of doing his
homework in crayon.

4. **altercation** (ôl tər kā´ shən) *n.* a heated argument
The mounting tension finally spawned an *altercation* between the police and the
residents.
syn: quarrel; dispute   *ant: agreement; harmony*

5. **ominous** (om´ ə nəs) *adj.* threatening; foreboding evil
We went on our picnic despite the *ominous* rain clouds.
syn: sinister   *ant: comforting*

6. **galvanize** (gal´ və nīz) *v.* to startle into sudden activity
A slight motion of the guard's rifle *galvanized* the lazy work crew into action.
syn: stimulate   *ant: enervate*

7. **exhort** (ig zôrt´) *v.* to urge on with stirring words
During halftime, the coach *exhorted* his team to "win one for the Gipper."
syn: encourage

8. **audacity** (ô das´ i tē) *n.* rude boldness; nerve
Kate's father was enraged when she had the *audacity* to talk back to him.
syn: insolence; impudence   *ant: decorum*

9. **evince** (i vins´) *v.* to demonstrate clearly; to prove
If you *evince* your theory, the university will fund your further studies.
syn: manifest

10. **hyperbole** (hī pûr´ bə lē) *n.* extreme exaggeration for effect and not meant to be
taken literally
When Susan told her son she was going to kill him, it was only *hyperbole*.
ant: understatement

11. **expedient** (ik spē´ dē ənt) *adj.* practical; providing an immediate advantage (especially when serving one's self-interest)
Lying, while not admirable, did prove to be the most *expedient* way to obtain the information.
syn: effective   *ant: feckless*

12. **incarcerate** (in kär´ sə rāt) *v.* to put into prison; to confine
We were shocked that the police *incarcerated* Rafael for something as minor as stealing hubcaps.
syn: imprison; constrain   *ant: liberate; free*

13. **incisive** (in sī´ siv) *adj.* sharp; keen; cutting straight to the heart of the matter
I had thought the meeting would run for hours, but Sharon made a few *incisive* comments that settled matters without wasting time or words.
syn: piercing; acute   *ant: superficial; dull*

14. **implacable** (im pla´ kə bəl) *adj.* unable to be appeased or pacified
Her *implacable* suspicions were finally put to rest when a private investigator assured her that her husband was faithful.
syn: inflexible; relentless   *ant: pacified; assuaged*

15. **pertinent** (pûr´ tn ənt) *adj.* having to do with the subject at hand; relevant
The lecturer took questions as long as they were *pertinent* and enriched the discussion.
         ant: unrelated; extraneous

Exercise I

Words in Context

From the list below, supply the words needed to complete the paragraph. Some words will not be used.

ominous	exhort	galvanize	hyperbole
expedient	implacable	incisive	hue

1. "What are you doing, you guys? I shouldn't have to _____ you at this point in the game!" _____ by Liza's scream, the four workers picked up their sanders and returned to their unfinished portions of drywall.

   "We're two days overdue! That means we're paying them now!" The worker closest to Liza turned a[n] _____ of red as she screamed. He knew that Liza's lecture was not merely _____ to get the team to work faster; the contractors really were beyond their deadline. Liza was worried for good reason; if the company couldn't prove that it was capable of _____, short-notice refurbishing, it would more than likely lose its contract with the city.

   Myron, the site foreman, appreciated Liza's _____ comments. At least she took the time to explain why the workers needed to labor more quickly. Such practice reminded the workers of just how small the degree of separation was between the company's success and their paychecks: It also prevented the workers from classifying Liza as a[n] _____ manager who just wanted to make a profit. If the workers knew that the company was suffering, they knew that their jobs were in jeopardy.

From the list below, supply the words needed to complete the paragraph. Some words will not be used.

altercation	lexicon	sanction	ominous	audacity
evince	incarcerate	pertinent	implacable	galvanize

2. Eugene had worked at the genetics lab for six days when he witnessed the noisy _____ between Dr. Strangeon and his research assistant.

   "You know that I didn't give _____ to an early run of the cloning module! Now you've destroyed the entire lot!" Strangeon was definitely irate, and Eugene wished that he understood more of the laboratory _____ that the doctor spouted at his assistant.

   "How could you—you're not an intern anymore—how could you have the _____ to go off on your own and initiate a test run of a model that required eight years of research and over twelve million dollars to develop? Well?" The assistant could only mutter an answer.

   "I just thought—I—uh—I wanted to see if—"

   "What you want is not _____ here!" shouted the doctor. "You've only managed to _____ the fact that you're unfit to work in a laboratory! We should press charges and have the police _____ you! Now get out!"

   The problem, thought Eugene, probably involved whatever Dr. Strangeon stored behind the _____ pair of tall, armored doors with the retina-scanning lock mechanism. Dr. Strangeon and his assistant had been the only two people to enter that room during the week that Eugene had been employed at the lab.

Exercise II

Sentence Completion

Complete the sentence in a way that shows you understand the meaning of the italicized vocabulary word.

1. To master the *lexicon* of the law, John...

2. Lonnie's face turned a sickly *hue* of green after...

3. The judge decided to *incarcerate* Tara because...

4. The *incisive* instructions made it easy for Lynn to...

5. The *expedience* the town showed in building a dam of sandbags...

6. The *ominous* gates in front of the old mansion made us...

7. *Galvanized* by the sound of the screaming foreman, the workers...

8. I don't need to *evince* my value at this company because...

9. Be sure to get *sanction* before you try to enter the...

10. During the peace talks, the *implacable* general refused...

11. The physical *altercation* between the brothers caused the neighbors to...

12. It seemed *hyperbole* to me when my teacher said...

13. The sergeant was advised to *exhort* the platoon prior to the...

14. The paramedics wanted only *pertinent* information because...

15. In the courtroom, the prisoner had the *audacity* to...

Exercise III

Roots, Prefixes, and Suffixes

Study the entries and answer the questions that follow.

The root *dorm* means "sleep."
The root *fin* means "end."
The suffix *–ory* means "a place for."
The root *nom* means "name."
The suffix *–ee* means "one who is."
The prefix *in–* means "not."
The root *clat* means "calling" or "system of calling."

1. Using *literal* translations as guidance, define the following words without using a dictionary:

    A. dormitory
    B. dormant
    C. nominee
    D. nomenclature
    E. finite
    F. infinite

2. You might see the grand *finale* at the _____ of a show.

3. Since the mayor-for-a-day position was only *nominal*, Colette could not
    _____.

4. List as many words as you can think of that contain the roots *dorm, fin,* and *nom.*

Exercise IV

Inference

Complete the sentences by inferring information about the italicized word from its context.

1. Judging by the debris on the highway and the intensity of the drivers' *altercation*, I assumed that the two drivers…

2. Mr. Moulan's *expedient* methods to get rich were probably to blame for…

3. If you don't have *sanction* to sell refreshments in the stadium, the security guards might…

Exercise V

Critical Reading

Below is a pair of reading passages followed by several multiple-choice questions. Carefully read the passages and choose the best answer for each of the questions.

The following passages, by Benjamin Franklin (1706–1790) and Francis Bacon (1561–1626) respectively, offer two perspectives on personal finance.

Passage 1

When I was a child of seven years old, my friends, on a holiday, filled my pocket with coppers. I went directly to a shop where they sold toys for children; and being charmed with the sound of a *whistle*, that I met by the way in the hands of another boy, I voluntarily offered and gave all my money for one. I then came home, and went whistling all over the house, much pleased
5 with my *whistle*, but disturbing all the family. My brothers, and sisters, and cousins, understanding the bargain I had made, told me I had given four times as much for it as it was worth; put me in mind what good things I might have bought with the rest of the money; and laughed at me so much for my folly, that I cried with vexation; and the reflection gave me more chagrin than the *whistle* gave me pleasure.

10 This, however, was afterwards of use to me, the impression continuing on my mind; so that often, when I was tempted to buy some unnecessary thing, I said to myself, *Don't give too much for the whistle*; and I saved my money.

As I grew up, came into the world, and observed the actions of men, I thought I met with many, very many, *who gave too much for the whistle.*

15 When I saw one too ambitious of court favor, sacrificing his time in attendance on levees, his repose, his liberty, his virtue, and perhaps his friends, to attain it, I have said to myself, *This man gives too much for his whistle.*

When I saw another fond of popularity, constantly employing himself in political bustles, neglecting his own affairs, and ruining them by that neglect, *He pays, indeed, said I, too much for*
20 *his whistle.*

If I knew a miser, who gave up every kind of comfortable living, all the pleasure of doing good to others, all the esteem of his fellow-citizens, and the joys of benevolent friendship, for the sake of accumulating wealth, *Poor man, said I, you pay too much for your whistle.*

When I met with a man of pleasure, sacrificing every laudable improvement of the mind, or
25 of his fortune, to mere corporeal sensations, and ruining his health in their pursuit, *Mistaken man,* said I, *you are providing pain for yourself, instead of pleasure; you give too much for your whistle.*

If I see one fond of appearance, or fine clothes, fine houses, fine furniture, fine equipages, all above his fortune, for which he contracts debts, and ends his career in a prison, *Alas!* say I, *he has paid dear, very dear, for his whistle.*

30 When I see a beautiful sweet-tempered girl married to an ill-natured brute of a husband, *What a pity, say I, that she should pay so much for a whistle!*

In short, I conceive that great part of the miseries of mankind are brought upon them by the false estimates they have made of the value of things, and by their *giving too much for their whistles.*

Yet I ought to have charity for these unhappy people, when I consider that, with all this wis-
35 dom of which I am boasting, there are certain things in the world so tempting, for example, the apples of King John, which happily are not to be bought; for if they were put to sale by auction, I might very easily be led to ruin myself in the purchase, and find that I had once more given too much for the *whistle*.

Passage 2

RICHES are for spending, and spending for honor and good actions. Therefore extraordinary expense must be limited by the worth of the occasion; for voluntary undoing may be as well for a man's country as for the kingdom of heaven. But ordinary expense ought to be limited by a man's estate; and governed with such regard, as it be within his compass; and not subject to deceit and
5　abuse of servants; and ordered to the best show, that the bills may be less than the estimation abroad. Certainly, if a man will keep but of even hand, his ordinary expenses ought to be but to the half of his receipts; and if he think to wax rich, but to the third part. It is no baseness for the greatest to descend and look into their own estate. Some forbear it, not upon negligence alone, but doubting to bring themselves into melancholy, in respect they shall find it broken. But wounds
10　cannot be cured without searching. He that cannot look into his own estate at all, had need both choose well those whom he employeth, and change them often; for new are more timorous and less subtle. He that can look into his estate but seldom, it behooveth him to turn all to certainties. A man had need, if he be plentiful in some kind of expense, to be as saving again in some other. As if he be plentiful in diet, to be saving in apparel; if he be plentiful in the hall, to be saving in
15　the stable; and the like. For he that is plentiful in expenses of all kinds will hardly be preserved from decay. In clearing of a man's estate, he may as well hurt himself in being too sudden, as in letting it run on too long. For hasty selling is commonly as disadvantageable as interest. Besides, he that clears at once will relapse; for finding himself out of straits, he will revert to his customs: but he that cleareth by degrees induceth a habit of frugality, and gaineth as well upon his mind as
20　upon his estate. Certainly, who hath a state to repair, may not despise small things; and commonly it is less dishonorable to abridge petty charges, than to stoop to petty gettings. A man ought warily to begin charges which once begun will continue; but in matters that return not he may be more magnificent.

1A.　As used in line 8 of the first passage, *vexation* most nearly means
　　A.　sadness.
　　B.　aggravation.
　　C.　anger.
　　D.　jealousy.
　　E.　power.

1B.　*Chagrin* (line 8), is related to Franklin's vexation. The best synonym for *chagrin* is
　　A.　joy.
　　B.　terror.
　　C.　embarrassment.
　　D.　humor.
　　E.　understanding.

2A.　According to passage 1, which of the following examples does *not* qualify as "giving too much for a whistle"?
　　A.　ruining one's ears by listening to loud music
　　B.　going bankrupt after purchasing a lavish home
　　C.　spending large amounts of money on gambling
　　D.　getting married before purchasing a home
　　E.　getting fired after stealing money from the workplace

2B. The details of the multiple scenarios Franklin provides suggests that there are many forms of
   A. comforting oneself for having lost whistles.
   B. currency to pay for one's whistle.
   C. obstacles to paying for whistles.
   D. unhappiness for not paying enough for whistles.
   E. boasting, especially about new whistles.

3A. The term "court favor" in line 15 of the first passage refers to
   A. popularity.
   B. judges.
   C. criminals.
   D. dating.
   E. sportsmanship.

3B. Which line from passage 1 best supports your answer to question 2A?
   A. "If I see one fond of appearance…"
   B. "…I was tempted to buy some unnecessary thing…"
   C. "…I had given four times as much for it as it was worth…"
   D. "…I ought to have charity…"
   E. "…I saw another fond of popularity…"

4A. In passage 1, the author uses a whistle as a metaphor for a
   A. tangible good.
   B. marketplace.
   C. want.
   D. person.
   E. child's toy.

4B. Based on passage 1, Franklin would probably agree with which one of the following statements?
   A. Sacrificing too much for something is healthy.
   B. It is noble to achieve goals at all costs.
   C. Overpaying for things gives the things more value to others.
   D. People often overestimate what things are worth.
   E. Some things are worth ruining one's reputation for.

5A. The best substitute for the word *baseness*, as it appears in line 7 of passage 2, is
   A. shame.
   B. debt.
   C. effort.
   D. insult.
   E. chore.

5B. Choose the most accurate paraphrase of the following quotation.

"Some forebear it [looking into their own estates], not upon negligence alone, but doubting to bring themselves into melancholy, in respect they shall find it broken."

    A.   Some people are too emotionally fragile to manage their own finances, so they hire others to run the estate.

    B.   Estate owners must have confidence and real concern for their property.

    C.   Those who endure the running of their own estates can become depressed.

    D.   Some people fail to examine their own estates because they are afraid their finances might be run poorly.

    E.   Running an estate is saddening because the owner usually feels that it is neglected.

6A. According to passage 2, one's routine expenses should not exceed

    A.   one-third of his income.

    B.   one-half of his income.

    C.   his income.

    D.   the cost of the servants' salaries.

    E.   the value of the estate.

6B. Keeping routine expenses below one-third of one's income is the strategy for what specific outcome, according to passage 2?

    A.   being charitable enough

    B.   ensuring servants are paid fairly

    C.   maintaining stability

    D.   becoming rich

    E.   running an estate

7A. Which of the choices is the most appropriate title for passage 2?

    A.   Pay Less for Your Whistle

    B.   Putting Your Money to Work

    C.   Saving is Essential

    D.   Spending Wisely

    E.   Perceiving Value

7B. If passage 2 were in a newspaper, it would appear under which section?

    A.   Real Estate

    B.   Politics

    C.   Business

    D.   Local News

    E.   Advice

8A. Which of the choices best paraphrases the following line from passage 2?

"A man had need, if he be plentiful in some kind of expense, to be as saving again in some other."

   A. A penny saved is a penny earned.
   B. People who have considerable debt should eliminate trivial expenses.
   C. A person who spends a lot of money on one thing needs to be frugal about other things.
   D. People should open savings accounts if they spend too much money.
   E. Spending too much money for one thing will limit one's ability to purchase other things.

8B. The *diet* and the *hall* mentioned in passage 2, line 14, would be labeled as what by Franklin, the author of passage 1?
   A. needs
   B. whistles
   C. charges
   D. miseries
   E. sensations

9. Which of the lines from passage 2 has the most similar meaning to the italicized portion of this example from passage 1?

"When I met with a man of pleasure, sacrificing every laudable improvement of the mind, or of his fortune, to mere corporeal sensations, and ruining his health in their pursuit, *Mistaken man, said I, you are providing pain for yourself, instead of pleasure; you give too much for your whistle.*"

   A. "Riches are for spending, and spending for honor and good actions." (line 1)
   B. "A man had need, if he be plentiful in some kind of expense, to be as saving again in some other." (line 13)
   C. "For hasty selling is commonly as disadvantageable as interest." (line 17)
   D. "In clearing of a man's estate, he may as well hurt himself in being too sudden, as in letting it run on too long." (lines 16-17)
   E. "A man ought warily to begin charges which once begun will continue; but in matters that return not he may be more magnificent." (lines 21-23)

10A. Which of the choices best describes the difference in intent between the passages?
   A. Passage 1 focuses on money, while passage 2 focuses on property.
   B. Passage 1, unlike passage 2, suggests a change in lifestyle.
   C. Passage 1 emphasizes value, while passage 2 emphasizes thrift.
   D. Passage 1 emphasizes frugality, while passage 2 emphasizes profit.
   E. Passage 1 is witty, while passage 2 is dull.

10B. Choose the statement that best describes the difference in the intended audiences of the two passages.

A. Passage 1 applies to anyone; passage 2 specifically advises estate owners.

B. Passage 1 caters to the poor, while passage 2 addresses the rich.

C. Passage 1 discusses politics, while passage 2 is strictly financial.

D. Passage 1 is a newspaper article, while passage 2 is probably from a book.

E. Passage 1 is written for Americans; passage 2 was written before America existed.

Vocabulary
Power Plus for
College and Career Readiness

LEVEL
TEN

Review Lessons 10-12

Exercise I

Inferences

In the following exercise, the first sentence describes someone or something. Infer information from the first sentence, and then choose the word from the Word Bank that best completes the second sentence.

altercation	hyperbole	incisive	dolorous
inscrutable	formidable	expound	humility

1. The government's explanation of the strange lights in the desert was far too vague to satisfy the local residents, who vowed to contact their congressional representatives if some real answers were not provided.

    From this sentence, we can infer that the citizens want the government to _____ on the explanation of the strange lights.

2. The fugitive would have escaped if not for his minor traffic accident with a very short-tempered driver, whose screaming caused a scene that drew the attention of every driver in the parking lot, including a police officer in a cruiser.

    From this sentence, we can infer that the _____ cost the fugitive a clean get-away.

3. The colonists hoped that the sight of their massive fort, bedecked with dozens of cannons, sniper holes, and watch towers, would dissuade the natives from attack.

    From this sentence, we can infer that the colonists created a[n] _____ image in an effort to avoid conflict.

4. Darlene said that there must have been more than a million people at the shoe store on the day of the big sale.

    From this sentence, we can infer that Darlene uses _____ in her descriptions.

5. The mystery behind the ancient pyramid in the jungle is what brings thousands of tourists to see it every year; it seems everyone has his or her own theory about the structure's intended purpose.

    From this sentence, we can infer that tourists are attracted to the landmark because of its _____ history.

Exercise II

Related Words

Some of the vocabulary words from Lessons 10 through 12 have related meanings. Complete the following sentences by choosing the word that best fits the context, based on information you infer from the use of the italicized word. Some word pairs will be antonyms, some will be synonyms, and some will simply be words often used in the same context.

1.   Historians discovered the lost *epistles* of the famous physicist, but only a few scientists could follow the obscure _____.
    A.   sycophant
    B.   altercation
    C.   hue
    D.   lexicon
    E.   sanction

2.   Jonah _____ on his plan to generate power from cold fusion before he *evinced* his theory by demonstrating a fully functioning reactor of his own design.
    A.   galvanized
    B.   balked
    C.   exulted
    D.   harangued
    E.   expounded

3.   The contractors quickly sprang from their after-lunch *lethargy* when their client _____ them by offering a large cash bonus if they completed the whole job by midnight.
    A.   balked
    B.   fluctuated
    C.   galvanized
    D.   exhorted
    E.   exulted

4.   The _____ Katie used during her *harangue* about the unfair science exam made the test sound as though not even a genius could have passed it.
    A.   epistle
    B.   hyperbole
    C.   hue
    D.   lexicon
    E.   sanction

5. The colonel marched his battered regiment northward to avoid a[n] _____
    with the colonial militias comprised of vengeful relatives and *formidable* marksmen.
    A. lexicon
    B. hue
    C. sanction
    D. acrimony
    E. altercation

6. The king's royal whisperer was a *sycophant* who acted as a social _____ in the
    evenings, learned the latest gossip and rumors, and reported it to his liege every day
    at lunch.
    A. gadfly
    B. hyperbole
    C. epistle
    D. lethargy
    E. altercation

7. The police _____ the crime family's lieutenant on a minor charge because he
    balked at testifying against his boss.
    A. galvanized
    B. incarcerated
    C. cajoled
    D. expounded
    E. exhorted

8. The mountain villagers could either make the _____ trek to town on foot
    through miles of rocky trails, or they could descend on the *expedient*, though fright-
    ening, zip line, suspended from the top of a cliff to the valley floor, far below.
    A. avid
    B. affable
    C. incisive
    D. arduous
    E. pertinent

9. The McCoys never *sanctioned* their daughter's marriage to the Hatfield boy because
    _____ between the families had rendered them enemies for the last fifteen
    years.
    A. audacity
    B. humility
    C. acrimony
    D. sycophant
    E. lethargy

10. Ophelia *exhorted* her friends in their most _____ moments, compassionately
    urging them to move forward and to live life once again.
    A. pertinent
    B. dolorous
    C. gargantuan
    D. grandiloquent
    E. affable

Exercise III

Deeper Meanings

Choose a word to replace the italicized word in each sentence. All of the possible choices for each sentence have similar definitions, but the correct answer will have a connotation that best suits the context. For example, the words "delete," "destroy," and "obliterate" all mean "to remove or wipe out," but no one would ever say, "I destroyed the name from the document." The correct choice will be the word that has the best specific meaning and does not render the sentence awkward in tone or content. When choices seem close, look for a clue in the context that makes one choice better than the other.

Note that the correct answer is not always the primary vocabulary word from the lesson.

harry	dour	perfect	frightening
tough	smart	ask	revenge
interrogate	rage	hatred	incisive
bothered	formidable		

1. Heather experienced instant *acrimony* and stormed off toward her brother's room when she noticed that he had been reading her diary.

    Better word: _____

2. If the player's *irritable* look was any indicator, then the team had just failed to win what should have been an easy district title.

    Better word: _____

3. The newspaper editor's job is to *plague* the reporters just enough that they finish their work ahead of deadlines, but not so much that they quit their jobs.

    Better word: _____

4. Charlotte's twenty years of experience as a head chef made her a[n] *scary* competitor in the iron skillet contest.

    Better word: _____

5. Rather than speaking in generic terms and vague examples, the teacher provided *keen* explanations to which students could relate at a personal level.

    Better word: _____

Exercise IV

Crossword Puzzle

Use the clues to complete the crossword puzzle. The answers consist of vocabulary words from Lessons 10 through 12.

Across

3. airborne pest?
6. out loud
8. what a scream does to a bat in your cave
10. humble ingredient
15. like a know-it-all
16. to bait
17. like a giant lizard approaching city limits
18. greasing the gears a little

Down

1. pat self on back
2. stop short
4. like a sodbuster
5. bad vibes
7. cloak-and-dagger look
9. E-mail?
11. throw in the slammer
12. Like it matters here.
13. bad kind of smile
14. You've seen this word a hundred times today.

Exercise V

Subject Prompts

Here is a writing prompt similar to the one you will find on the writing portion of an assessment test. Follow the instructions below and write a brief, efficient essay.

> When schools face budget cuts, which programs should be the first to go, and why? Extracurricular activities, of course, are typically the first programs to be terminated, but should that be the case? Should sports and music programs have a lower priority than other parts of the curriculum (other than the core curriculum of math, science, and English)?
>
> Write a letter to a school board and suggest which programs, types of programs, or parts of the curriculum should be the first to be cut. Think of at least three candidates for termination, and explain in detail why each one should not be spared. Consider the ultimate benefit of the programs to the education of the students.

Thesis: Write a *one-sentence* response to the above assignment. Make certain this single sentence offers a clear statement of your position.

Example: The first programs to be cut should be the ones least relevant to the majority of employers.

_____

_____

Organizational Plan: List at least three subtopics you will use to support your main idea. This list is your outline.

1. _____

2. _____

3. _____

Draft: Following your outline, write a good first draft of your essay. Remember to support all your points with examples, facts, references to reading, etc.

Review and Revise: Exchange essays with a classmate. Using the scoring guide for Word Choice on page 261, score your partner's essay (while he or she scores yours). Focus on word choice and the use of language conventions. If necessary, rewrite your essay to improve word choice and/or your use of language.

Lesson Thirteen

1. **circumvent** (sûr kəm vent´) *v.* to get around; to bypass
Though she did not lie, the defendant *circumvented* the question by claiming she could not remember where she was at the time.
syn: avoid

2. **inert** (in ûrt´) *adj.* unable to act or move; inactive; sluggish
All dangerous components have been removed from the *inert* missile on display at the science museum.
syn: dormant; passive   *ant: dynamic; active*

3. **latent** (lāt´ nt) *adj.* present, but not active; hidden
After retiring, Nat took up painting and found that he had had *latent* artistic talents all along.
syn: dormant   *ant: manifest*

4. **acquit** (ə kwit´) *v.* to find not guilty of a fault or crime
The jury *acquitted* the man, and he was free to go.
syn: absolve   *ant: convict*

5. **deprecate** (dep´ ri kāt) *v.* to express strong disapproval of
Doug stopped offering new ideas after the other workers *deprecated* his first suggestion.
syn: deplore   *ant: approve; praise*

6. **barrister** (bar´ i stər) *n.* lawyer (British)
The *barrister* questioned the witness as to his familiarity with a certain London pub.

7. **adulation** (aj ōō lā´ shən) *n.* excessive praise or admiration
Kim despised the *adulation* heaped on rock stars by young fans.
syn: flattery; adoration   *ant: derision*

8. **artful** (art´ fəl) *adj.* slyly clever; crafty
The *artful* investor didn't make many friends, but he had earned his first million dollars before he reached the age of twenty-one.
syn: sharp; shrewd   *ant: naive; clumsy*

9. **culinary** (kul´ ə ner ē) *adj.* having to do with the kitchen or cooking
The famous chef had been a life-long student of the *culinary* arts.

10. **chastise** (chas tīz´) *v.* to punish severely
Professor Jacques *chastised* Archie for skipping Latin and gave him ten extra chapters to translate.
syn: discipline

11. **bawdy** (bô´ dē) *adj.* indecent; humorously obscene
When some called the new sitcom *bawdy*, the toy company quickly withdrew its sponsorship.
syn: risqué; lewd   *ant: innocent; clean*

12. **frugal** (frōō´ gəl) *adj.* thrifty; economical in money matters
My *frugal* father buys only day-old bread and marked-down fruit.
syn: economical   *ant: wasteful; profligate*

13. **jocose** (jō kōs´) *adj.* joking; humorous
Gary's *jocose* manner often led people to say he should become a stand-up comedian.
syn: witty; funny; playful; jocund   *ant: serious*

14. **myriad** (mir´ ē əd) *n.* a very large number *adj.* too numerous to be counted
(*n.*) After my break-up, my mom fed me the old line about there being a
    myriad of fish in the sea.
(*adj.*)The biologist spent her entire career categorizing the *myriad* plant species of the
    rain forest.
(*n.*) *syn: host; multitude*
(*adj.*)*syn: countless; innumerable*   *ant: few; limited*

15. **pernicious** (pər nish´ əs) *adj.* destructive; deadly
The *pernicious* plague wiped out half the country's population.
syn: malignant; harmful   *ant: benign*

Exercise I

Words in Context

From the list below, supply the words needed to complete the paragraph. Some words will not be used.

culinary	pernicious	latent	frugal	circumvent
artful	inert	jocose	myriad	

1. Like a[n] _____ saboteur hiding in plain sight in enemy territory, waiting for the go-ahead signal, the tiny microorganism infiltrated the deepest, most vulnerable parts of its host and remained in a dormant state. Waves of red blood cells knocked the _____ bacterium about, tossing its _____, suspended form from one membrane to the next. The germ waited, as it had for days, until the host's chemistry was perfect for waking from its slumber and unleashing its _____ poison in the host's body. In a few hours, the single microbe would multiply into _____ bundles of destruction, and then the tiny legion would seize control of the host's nervous system. Not even the best research scientists could find a way to _____ the deadly effects of the microscopic villains.

From the list below, supply the words needed to complete the paragraph. Some words will not be used.

adulation	frugal	acquit	myriad
jocose	barrister	chastise	deprecate

2. "What are you being so _____ about? We're in a courtroom, you fool; shut up."
   Scolded by his only friend in the room, Giles stopped laughing but maintained his crooked smirk. His _____ was quickly losing patience; both he and Giles knew that there was no chance that the judge was going to _____ him. This was his second appearance before Justice Quentin, and by the way in which the judge _____ Giles during the previous trial, he knew that he wasn't going to get away this time. As the smirk faded, Giles wished that he hadn't been so _____ while shopping for lawyers.

From the list below, supply the words needed to complete the paragraph. Some words will not be used.

frugal	bawdy	adulation
artful	deprecate	culinary

3. Theme restaurants do not usually become popular for the quality of their cuisine, but the Gold Mine, operated in the likeness of a California gold-rush saloon, has received the _____ of every food critic who has eaten there. The saloon is one of few tourism-dependent restaurants that gives as much attention to its _____ performance as to the nightly stage shows featuring vaudeville-style comedians, singers, and cancan dancers wearing the _____ saloon outfits of the period. After twenty years of service, few patrons—if any—have been able to _____ the quality of food and entertainment at the Gold Mine.

Exercise II

Sentence Completion

Complete the sentence in a way that shows you understand the meaning of the italicized vocabulary word.

1. My *bawdy* uncle really didn't fit in at the…

2. The *barrister* feared his client's associates after…

3. As the fallen disco ball struck the floor, a *myriad* of…

4. No one thought that it was too extreme to *chastise* Gary for…

5. The *artful* pickpocket had the most success when…

6. The *latent* saboteur waited for the signal to…

7. Pete was *acquitted* of the crime, but the general public still believed…

8. The swarm of *pernicious* locusts caused the farmer to…

9. The crowd's *adulation* for Monique revealed her…

11. Some people laugh at Ken, but others find his *jocose* manner to be…

12. Richard was so *frugal* that he refused to…

13. Feel free to *deprecate* my idea now, but not when we're in front of…

14. When you finish using the *culinary* utensils, please…

15. The *inert* Jose lay on the couch after an exhausting day of…

15. To *circumvent* the broken power line, the electric company…

Exercise III

Roots, Prefixes, and Suffixes

Study the entries and answer the questions that follow.

The roots *fac, fact, fect,* and *fic* mean "make" or "do."
The root *grat* means "please."
The suffix *–tude* means "the state of."
The roots *mot* and *mov* mean "to move."
The prefix *con–* means "with."
The prefix *re–* means "away."
The prefix *de–* means "down."

1. Using *literal* translations as guidance, define the following words without using a dictionary:

    A. factory   D. motivation
    B. gratitude   E. remote
    C. congratulations   F. demote

2. A person who does certain activities very well can be said to have a _____ for them. If you ease the progress of a class meeting, you could be called a[n] _____.

3. If you are feeling thankful for someone's help, you might describe yourself as feeling _____.

4. List as many words as you can think of that contain the roots *fac, fact, fect, fic,* or *grat.*

Exercise IV

Inference

Complete the sentences by inferring information about the italicized word from its context.

1. If Eddie's parents *chastise* him by taking away his car keys, you might assume that Eddie…

2. If the foreman usually *deprecates* the behavior of his employees, the workers will probably…

3. When a *myriad* of sparks emerged from beneath her car, Lanna was glad that she…

Exercise V

Writing

Here is a writing prompt similar to the one you will find on the writing portion of an assessment test.

Plan and write an essay based on the following statement:

> And then there were books, a kind of parallel universe in which anything might happen and frequently did, a universe in which I might be a newcomer but was never really a stranger. My real, true world.
>
> –Anna Quindlen
> *How Reading Changed My Life* (1998)

Assignment: Think of a book in which you felt you had discovered your real, true world. Write an essay describing how that is so. Use elements of plot, character, and setting to form your discussion, and be sure to consider books of all genres, including fiction, nonfiction, songs, drama, and poetry.

Thesis: Write a *one-sentence* response to the above assignment. Make certain this single sentence offers a clear statement of your position.

Example: J.R.R. Tolkien's The Lord of the Rings *trilogy is sometimes more real to me than the world I live in because it inspires me to seek the inner hero in myself.*

_____

_____

Organizational Plan: List at least three subtopics you will use to support your main idea. This list is your outline.

1. _____

2. _____

3. _____

Draft: Following your outline, write a good first draft of your essay. Remember to support all your points with examples, facts, references to reading, etc.

Review and Revise: Exchange essays with a classmate. Using the scoring guide for Development on page 258, score your partner's essay (while he or she scores yours). Focus on the development of ideas and the use of language conventions. If necessary, rewrite your essay to incorporate more (or more relevant) support and/or improve your use of language.

Exercise VI

English Practice

Identifying Sentence Errors

Identify the grammatical error in each of the following sentences. If the sentence contains no error, select answer choice E.

1. When I met my uncle, I was shocked to see that he doesn't have hardly any hair.
         (A)   (B)   (C)   (D)
    No error
      (E)

2. When my mother went to do the shopping, I would of cleaned my room,
          (A)   (B)   (C)
    but I fell asleep.   No error
        (D)   (E)

3. The stationery part of the clock is in the center, but the outer edge rotates
              (A)   (B)   (C)
    with every passing second.   No error
                  (D)   (E)

4. My father said I could associate with whoever I wanted, as long as I didn't bring
                   (A)   (B)   (C)
    anyone home for dinner.   No error
                     (D)   (E)

5. Any woman who doesn't meet the necessary requirements will have their name
        (A)   (B)   (C)
    removed from the list of candidates.   No error
            (D)   (E)

Improving Sentences

The underlined portion of each sentence below contains some flaw. Select the answer choice that best corrects the flaw.

6. Sleeping peacefully, we finally located the lost puppy in an abandoned mine tunnel.
    A.   Sleeping peacefully, we located the puppy finally in an abandoned mine tunnel.
    B.   In an abandoned mine tunnel, we finally located the lost puppy sleeping peacefully.
    C.   We finally located the lost puppy sleeping peacefully in an abandoned mine tunnel.
    D.   Finally in an abandoned mine tunnel we found sleeping peacefully the lost puppy.
    E.   We located the puppy lost in an abandoned mine tunnel finally sleeping peacefully.

7. The coach, along with the managers and team members, <u>were praised during the varsity sports banquet</u>.
   A. were praised for their performance during the varsity sports banquet.
   B. was praised during the varsity sports banquet.
   C. was praised for their performance during the varsity sports banquet.
   D. were praised during the Varsity Sports Banquet.
   E. was praised for their performance during the season.

8. <u>Our outdoor party quickly went inside when news of the approaching tornado was received by us</u>.
   A. When our outdoor party went inside, we quickly heard news of an approaching tornado.
   B. When we quickly went inside, our outdoor party news was an approaching tornado.
   C. An approaching tornado was news when our outdoor party went inside quickly.
   D. Our outdoor party, when news of an approaching tornado went quickly, we went inside.
   E. When we received news of an approaching tornado, our outdoor party quickly went inside.

9. <u>A suitcase was seen floating on Milltown Creek, but no one knew who's it was</u>.
   A. A suitcase was seen floating on Milltown Creek, but no one knew whose it was.
   B. No one knew who's suitcase was seen on Milltown Creek floating.
   C. Floating on Milltown Creek was seen a suitcase, but no one knew who's it was.
   D. Milltown Creek was seen with a floating suitcase, but no one knew who's it was.
   E. Who's suitcase was seen floating on Milltown Creek?

10. <u>Finding a bag of sandwiches in the bank vault, while the police were investigating a bank robbery</u>.
    A. A bag of sandwiches in the bank vault while police were investigating a bank robbery were found.
    B. In the bank vault, police investigating a bank robbery, finding a bag of sandwiches.
    C. While investigating a bag of sandwiches, police were found in the bank vault robbery.
    D. While investigating a bank robbery, police found a bag of sandwiches in the bank vault.
    E. The bank vault, a bag of sandwiches, and the police in a robbery investigation.

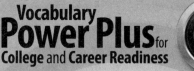
Lesson Fourteen

1. **enraptured** (en rap´ chərd) *adj.* delighted beyond measure
Sasha was *enraptured* by the performance of the visiting ballet troupe.
syn: ecstatic

2. **charlatan** (shär´ lə ten) *n.* one who pretends to have knowledge in order to swindle others
The supposed doctor endorsing the fat-burning "miracle drug" was actually a *charlatan*.
syn: quack; fraud   *ant: professional*

3. **hoax** (hōks) *n.* a practical joke; a trick
The sighting of Elvis at the Bowl-O-Rama turned out to be a *hoax*.
syn: fraud; fake

4. **obstreperous** (ob strep´ ər əs) *adj.* aggressively boisterous; stubborn and defiant
The *obstreperous* demonstrators were forced to move by an icy blast from the fire hose.
     ant: meek; tractable

5. **novice** (nov´ is) *n.* a beginner; one who is inexperienced
The older lawyer took the *novice* under her wing and showed him the ropes.
syn: apprentice; tyro   *ant: master*

6. **marital** (mar´ i təl) *adj.* having to do with marriage
Marital problems can sometimes be solved by a session with a marriage counselor.
syn: wedded   *ant: single*

7. **naïve** (nä ēv´) *adj.* simple in outlook; not affected or worldly; especially innocent
Old movies usually portray country girls in the city as *naïve* and vulnerable.
syn: unsophisticated; unsuspecting   *ant: sophisticated; cunning*

8. **genial** (jēn´ yəl) *adj.* friendly; amiable
Our new neighbors were so *genial* that we felt we had known them for years.
syn: cordial   *ant: unfriendly*

9. **amicable** (am´ i kə bəl) *adj.* friendly; peaceable
Commerce will suffer until the two nations establish *amicable* relations.
syn: agreeable; amiable   *ant: quarrelsome; warlike*

10. **mundane** (mun dān´) *adj.* commonplace; earthly and not spiritual
Virginia thought herself too good an artist to be expected to deal with *mundane* things like earning a living.
syn: boring   *ant: unique*

11. **fickle**   (fik´ əl)   *adj.*   likely to change on a whim or without apparent reason
Because she never kept one boyfriend for long, her friends said Keisha was *fickle*.
syn: vacillating; capricious   *ant: steadfast*

12. **levity**   (lev´ i tē)   *n.*   lightness of disposition; lack of seriousness
Kent brought an air of *levity* to the otherwise somber proceedings by cracking a few jokes.
syn: frivolity   *ant: sobriety; somberness*

13. **juggernaut**   (jug´ ər nôt)   *n.*   a terrible destructive or irresistible force
The Nazi *juggernaut* swept through Belgium and into France.

14. **nocturnal**   (nok tûr´ nəl)   *adj.*   having to do with the night; occurring at night
Owls are *nocturnal* creatures; they sleep during the day.
                              ant: diurnal

15. **bask**   (bask)   *v.*   to expose oneself to pleasant warmth
During the Florida vacation, all she did was *bask* in the sun.

Exercise I

Words in Context

From the list below, supply the words needed to complete the paragraph. Some words will not be used.

charlatan	naïve	enraptured	hoax	amicable
levity	bask	fickle	mundane	

1. When the _____ citizens of Reynoldsville finally realized that their forty-cent bottles of miracle sap contained nothing more than licorice extract and whiskey, they formed a lynch mob and searched for the _____ who had sold the fake elixir. Unfortunately, Colonel Britton, the quack they were looking for, had already taken his wagon and quietly left town before dawn. He rode nonstop for a full day until, in his usual routine, he pulled far off the trail and spent a day restocking his miracle sap, occasionally breaking to partake of some himself. _____ by the beautiful scenery of the Black Hills, Britton didn't waste his opportunity to _____ in the low autumn sun for the remainder of the afternoon. While most of his clientele were desensitized to the beauty of nature after spending harsh lives in it, Britton never once considered his private outings to be _____; if he didn't spend at least a few hours enjoying nature every week, he had trouble maintaining his _____ demeanor whenever he rolled into a new town. If Britton didn't at least appear to be happy, people were not going to purchase his tonic, whether it was a[n] _____ or not. His customers were very _____ about spending their money; if they had even the slightest notion that Britton's product was a scam, they would not buy it.

From the list below, supply the words needed to complete the paragraph. Some words will not be used.

genial	enraptured	nocturnal	obstreperous
novice	juggernaut	marital	levity

2. Despite her position as regional manager for Tyndall Systems, Shawna felt like a[n] _____ every time she attended the monthly sales meeting at Tyndall corporate headquarters. Perhaps she was just getting old, she reasoned, but she knew that few could endure her _____ schedule six days out of the week. Tyndall was a[n] _____ in the information technology arena, buying and consolidating other corporations and firing dissenters with impunity. Shawna told her husband that she would retire in two years; she hoped in time to mitigate their rapidly multiplying _____ problems. She was no longer the hard worker that Tyndall wanted for managing a regional hub, and the stress from trying to meet the demand had caused her once _____ manner to reverse—not that she needed it any more at the office. District sales meetings were not a place for _____; the twelve other managers spoke and carried themselves like assertive robots, rarely allowing jokes or laughter to interrupt their lengthy meetings. The single and most recent show of emotion at the meeting occurred when the vice president fired one of the managers on the spot, and the security guards had to drag him, _____ and screaming, out of the conference room.

Exercise II

Sentence Completion

Complete the sentence in a way that shows you understand the meaning of the italicized vocabulary word.

1. Our *genial* neighbor always invites us…

2. The *juggernaut* of tanks rolled effortlessly through…

3. The Clarks revealed few *marital* problems, but I knew that…

4. The *fickle* customers will not return to the store if…

5. The *nocturnal* raccoons waited…

6. The zookeepers struggled to move the *obstreperous* lion to…

7. Jules, an amateur chef, was *enraptured* by the master chef's invitation to…

8. Your *levity* in the present situation is…

9. No one ever would have guessed that the *charlatan* was not really a…

10. Mount Everest is not a place for *novice*…

11. The *naïve* young soldier had difficulty accepting…

12. When the ambulance pulled up, everyone knew that Kristen's *hoax* had…

13. The job might be *mundane*, but the city is…

14. Instead of attacking, the *amicable* natives…

15. Katie *basked* in the bright August sun until she…

Exercise III

Roots, Prefixes, and Suffixes

Study the entries and answer the questions that follow.

The root *hydr* means "water."
The root *junct* means "join."
The suffix *–phobia* means "fear of."
The prefix *de–* means "down," "away from," "about."
The prefixes *dis–, di–,* and *dif–* mean "apart" or "not."
The prefix *con–* means "with."

1. Using *literal* translations as guidance, define the following words without using a dictionary:

   A. dehydration   D. conjunction
   B. hydrophobia   E. juncture
   C. disjointed   F. hydroelectric

2. *Hydraulics* is the branch of physics that deals with _____ .

3. *Therm* is a root that means "heat"; therefore, *hydrothermal* has to do with

   _____ .

4. List as many words as you can think of that contain the roots *hydr* and *junct*.

Exercise IV

Inference

Complete the sentences by inferring information about the italicized word from its context.

1. If people respond to Myra's *levity* with angry glares, it is because she shouldn't be…

2. If the police determine that the suspicious package is a *hoax*, then it is probably safe for the evacuated employees to…

3. All the drivers waiting on the highway honked their horns because the farmer couldn't get the *obstreperous*…

Exercise V

Critical Reading

Below is a reading passage followed by several multiple-choice questions. Carefully read the passage and choose the best answer for each of the questions.

The following is an excerpt adapted from Mark Twain's satirical essay, "On the Decay of the Art of Lying." Twain discusses the types of truth that people do—and do not—want to hear.

Observe, I do not mean to suggest that the *custom* of lying has suffered any decay or interruption—no, for the Lie, as a Virtue, a Principle, is eternal; the Lie, as a recreation, a solace, a refuge in time of need, the fourth Grace, the tenth Muse, man's best and surest friend, is immortal, and cannot perish from the earth while this club remains. My complaint simply concerns the decay
5 of the *art* of lying. No high-minded man, no man of right feeling, can contemplate the lumbering and slovenly lying of the present day without grieving to see a noble art so prostituted. In this veteran presence I naturally enter upon this theme with diffidence; it is like an old maid trying to teach nursery matters to the mothers in Israel. It would not become to me to criticize you, gentlemen—who are nearly all my elders—and my superiors, in this thing—if I should here and
10 there *seem* to do it, I trust it will in most cases be more in a spirit of admiration than fault-finding; indeed if this finest of the fine arts had everywhere received the attention, the encouragement, and conscientious practice and development which this club has devoted to it, I should not need to utter this lament, or shed a single tear. I do not say this to flatter: I say it in a spirit of just and appreciative recognition. (It had been my intention, at this point, to mention names and to give
15 illustrative specimens, but indications observable about me admonished me to beware of the particulars and confine myself to generalities.)

No fact is more firmly established than that lying is a necessity of our circumstances—the deduction that it is then a Virtue goes without saying. No virtue can reach its highest usefulness without careful and diligent cultivation—therefore, it goes without saying that this one ought to
20 be taught in the public schools—even in the newspapers. What chance has the ignorant uncultivated liar against the educated expert? What chance have I against Mr. Per—against a lawyer? *Judicious* lying is what the world needs. I sometimes think it were even better and safer not to lie at all than to lie injudiciously. An awkward, unscientific lie is often as ineffectual as the truth.

Now let us see what the philosophers say. Note that venerable proverb: Children and fools
25 *always* speak the truth. The deduction is plain—adults and wise persons *never* speak it. Parkman, the historian, says, "The principle of truth may itself be carried into an absurdity." In another place in the same chapters he says, "The saying is old that truth should not be spoken at all times; and those whom a sick conscience worries into habitual violation of the maxim are imbeciles and nuisances." It is strong language, but true. None of us could *live* with an habitual truth-teller;
30 but thank goodness none of us has to. An habitual truth-teller is simply an impossible creature; he does not exist; he never has existed. Of course there are people who *think* they never lie, but it is not so—and this ignorance is one of the very things that shame our so-called civilization. Everybody lies—every day; every hour; awake; asleep; in his dreams; in his joy; in his mourning; if he keeps his tongue still, his hands, his feet, his eyes, his attitude, will convey deception—and
35 purposely. Even in sermons—but that is a platitude.

In a far country where I once lived the ladies used to go around paying calls, under the humane and kindly pretense of wanting to see each other; and when they returned home, they would cry out with a glad voice, saying, "We made sixteen calls and found fourteen of them

out"—not meaning that they found out anything important against the fourteen—no, that was
40 only a colloquial phrase to signify that they were not at home—and their manner of saying it
expressed their lively satisfaction in that fact. Now their pretense of wanting to see the fourteen—
and the other two whom they had been less lucky with—was that commonest and mildest form of
lying which is sufficiently described as a deflection from the truth. Is it justifiable? Most certainly.
It is beautiful, it is noble; for its object is, *not* to reap profit, but to convey a pleasure to the sixteen.
45 The iron-souled truth monger would plainly manifest, or even utter the fact that he didn't want to
see those people—and he would be an ass, and inflict totally unnecessary pain. And next, those
ladies in that far country—but never mind, they had a thousand pleasant ways of lying, that grew
out of gentle impulses, and were a credit to their intelligence and an honor to their hearts. Let the
particulars go.

50 The men in that far country were liars, every one. Their mere howdy-do was a lie, because
they didn't care how you did, except they were undertakers. To the ordinary inquirer you lied
in return; for you made no conscientious diagnostic of your case, but answered at random, and
usually missed it considerably. You lied to the undertaker, and said your health was failing—a
wholly commendable lie, since it cost you nothing and pleased the other man. If a stranger called
55 and interrupted you, you said with your hearty tongue, "I'm glad to see you," and said with your
heartier soul, "I wish you were with the cannibals and it was dinner-time." When he went, you
said regretfully, "*Must* you go?" and followed it with a "Call again"; but you did no harm, for
you did not deceive anybody nor inflict any hurt, whereas the truth would have made you both
unhappy.

60 I think that all this courteous lying is a sweet and loving art, and should be cultivated. The
highest perfection of politeness is only a beautiful edifice, built, from the base to the dome, of
graceful and gilded forms of charitable and unselfish lying.

What I bemoan is the growing prevalence of the brutal truth. Let us do what we can
to eradicate it. An injurious truth has no merit over an injurious lie. Neither should ever be
65 uttered. The man who speaks an injurious truth lest his soul be not saved if he do otherwise,
should reflect that that sort of a soul is not strictly worth saving. The man who tells a lie to help
a poor devil out of trouble, is one of whom the angels doubtless say, "Lo, here is an heroic soul
who casts his own welfare in jeopardy to succor his neighbor's; let us exalt this magnanimous
liar."

70 An injurious lie is an uncommendable thing; and so, also, and in the same degree, is an
injurious truth—a fact that is recognized by the law of libel.

Joking aside, I think there is much need of wise examination into what sorts of lies are best
and wholesomest to be indulged, seeing we *must* all lie and we *do* all lie, and what sorts it may
be best to avoid—and this is a thing which I feel I can confidently put into the hands of this
75 experienced Club—a ripe body, who may be termed, in this regard, and without undue flattery,
Old Masters.

1A. In mythology, the nine *muses* are the goddesses of inspiration once thought to bring ideas to writers, artists, and scientists. Which choice best describes what is accomplished when the lie is called a *muse* in line 3?
   A.   The lie is portrayed as archaic and unbelievable.
   B.   The author suggests that lying is really a form of truth.
   C.   The author expresses his moral disgust at the thought of lying.
   D.   The author portrays lying as a character flaw of women.
   E.   The author suggests that lying should be considered an art form.

1B. If your answer to question 1A is true, then lying is portrayed as
   A.   declining, because no one believes in muses.
   B.   improving every day with increases in population.
   C.   an active and embedded part of human nature.
   D.   merely one step toward the discovery of truth.
   E.   a nuisance that complicates the lives visited by the muse.

2A. In this passage, the author's intended audience is
   A.   a room full of workers at a staff meeting.
   B.   a newspaper editor he accuses of lying.
   C.   a classroom full of teenagers.
   D.   a group of habitual liars.
   E.   the guests at a political nomination.

2B. Choose the phrase that best supports your answer to question 2A.
   A.   "an old maid trying to teach nursery matters to the mothers"
   B.   "I should not need to utter this lament, or shed a single tear"
   C.   "I say it in a spirit of just and appreciative recognition"
   D.   "the Lie…cannot perish from the earth while this club remains"
   E.   "I do not mean to suggest that the *custom* of lying has suffered any decay"

3A. Which choice best explains why the author likens himself to an "old maid" in lines 7-10?
   A.   He likens himself to an inexperienced person attempting to teach experienced people.
   B.   The mythical *muses* are thousands of years old, and he compares himself to one.
   C.   The use of a female figure relates to his mostly female audience.
   D.   He wants to relate to the elders among his audience.
   E.   He relates the art of lying to typical communication among family members.

3B. In the author's "old maid" metaphor, the "mothers" are intended to represent
   A.   the nine other muses not mentioned in the passage.
   B.   the experienced liars of the club.
   C.   those responsible for the decay of the art of lying.
   D.   everyone in the world.
   E.   the defenders of the truth.

4A. Based on how it is used in line 7, the most accurate meaning of the word
diffidence is
    A.   diversity.
    B.   anger.
    C.   rigor.
    D.   arrogance.
    E.   reluctance.

4B. In line 9, "this thing" refers to
    A.   the organization.
    B.   public speaking.
    C.   providing criticism.
    D.   proficiency in lying.
    E.   the history of Greek myths.

5A. According to the author's rationale in lines 17-20, a *virtue* is legitimate if it is
    A.   repeated.
    B.   needed.
    C.   forgotten.
    D.   studied.
    E.   misused.

5B. To ensure the proper cultivation of virtues, including lying, the author prescribes
    A.   practice.
    B.   abstinence.
    C.   boldness.
    D.   laughter.
    E.   reading.

6A. The tone of this passage is best described as
    A.   pedantic and scholarly.
    B.   authoritative and impartial.
    C.   confident and scornful.
    D.   learned and informative.
    E.   foolish and nostalgic.

6B. If read at face value, the tone of the passage differs from the tone established if the audience realizes the author's lengthy farce, in which he prescribes dishonesty as a moral imperative. The genre of literature that best describes the passage is
    A.   history.
    B.   satire.
    C.   fiction.
    D.   memoir.
    E.   science.

7. In the passage, the author makes a distinction between the act of *lying* and the act of *deceiving*, with the latter being described as wrongful (line 70). According to lines 50-59, a lie is a "commendable" lie as long as which set of criteria is met?
   A. It happens naturally and has true meaning.
   B. It is shallow, intentionally awkward, and exaggerated.
   C. It costs nothing, gives pleasure, and hurts no one.
   D. It is pleasant, not an "undertaker" lie, and doesn't include cannibals.
   E. It is simple enough to be seen as a lie and causes no harm.

8A. Choose the best alternative title for this passage.
   A. The Case for Brutal Truth
   B. The Immorality of Deceit
   C. The Truth Hurts
   D. Foolish Honesty
   E. International Lying

8B. Which statement best expounds on your answer to question 8A?
   A. If you have to lie, make it hurt.
   B. Two lies make a right, so always lie.
   C. Never lie to an undertaker.
   D. Judicious lies are ineffectual.
   E. If the truth will hurt someone, tell a lie instead.

8C. Choose the sentence from the passage that best exemplifies your answer to question 8B.
   A. "I think that all this courteous lying is a sweet and loving art, and should be cultivated."
   B. "Their mere howdy-do was a lie, because *they* didn't care how you did, except they were undertakers."
   C. "If a stranger called and interrupted you, you said with your hearty tongue, 'I'm glad to see you,' and said with your heartier soul, 'I wish you were with the cannibals and it was dinner-time.' "
   D. "An injurious lie is an uncommendable thing...."
   E. "An injurious truth has no merit over an injurious lie."

9A. The organization of this essay is best described as
   A. chronological.
   B. cause and effect
   C. biographical
   D. problem and solution
   E. step by step.

9B. Choose the one title that fails to describe any of the essay's paragraph topics.
   A. The Necessity of Lying
   B. The Expert's Opinion on Lying
   C. Lying is Endangered
   D. Examples of Good Lies
   E. When to Tell Fewer Lies

10. Which type of publication is this passage most suited for?
    A.   a newspaper opinion column
    B.   a book on etiquette
    C.   a psychology journal
    D.   a religious newsletter
    E.   a newspaper political column

Lesson Fifteen

1. **connive** (kə nīv´) *v.* to cooperate secretly in wrongdoing
   The corrupt judge *connived* with crooked politicians in order to make himself rich.
   syn: conspire

2. **noxious** (nok´ shəs) *adj.* harmful to the health
   We opened a window to remove the *noxious* fumes of the paint thinner.
   syn: injurious   *ant: harmless*

3. **indiscreet** (in di skrēt´) *adj.* not wise or judicious; imprudent, as in speech or
       action
   Ron was fired shortly after his *indiscreet* actions at the office party.
   syn: flagrant; tactless   *ant: prudent*

4. **liege** (lēj) *n.* a lord, master, or sovereign
   While the servants pledged their loyalty to their *liege*, they did not always like or
   respect him.
   syn: king   *ant: commoner; servant*

5. **crass** (kras) *adj.* coarse; tasteless
   Ben made a *crass* comment about the length of the waitress's skirt.
   syn: crude   *ant: refined*

6. **chutzpah** (hoot´ spə) *n.* nerve; audacity
   I cannot believe Michael had the *chutzpah* to claim that no one could sing that song
   as well as he could.
   syn: brazenness; effrontery   *ant: timidity*

7. **fallacy** (fal´ ə sē) *n.* a mistaken notion; a misconception
   My grandmother still clings to the *fallacy* that the world is flat.
                                                      ant: truth

8. **complacent** (kəm plā´ sənt) *adj.* self-satisfied; smug
   The former heavyweight champion became *complacent* after easily defeating several
   amateur boxers.
   syn: assured; confident   *ant: humble*

9. **odium** (ō´ dē əm) *n.* hatred
   The rebels had only *odium* for the ruling party.
   syn: abhorrence   *ant: love; adoration*

10. **hypercritical** (hī pər krit´ i kəl) *adj.* overcritical; too severe in judgment
In his inspection of the barracks, the sergeant was so *hypercritical* that no one passed.
syn: faultfinding   *ant: lax*

11. **befuddle** (bi fud´ l) *v.* to confuse; to perplex
Street maps always *befuddle* me, so my girlfriend navigates when we take road trips.
syn: bewilder; fluster   *ant: clarify; elucidate*

12. **laudable** (lô´ də bəl) *adj.* worthy of praise; commendable
The city has made *laudable* efforts to reduce crime by introducing after-school programs.
syn: admirable   *ant: execrable*

13. **pandemonium** (pan də mō´ nē əm) *n.* a wild disorder, noise, or confusion
Feeding time at the zoo could be *pandemonium* if not done slowly and carefully.
syn: chaos; tumult; din   *ant: order; calm*

14. **parsimonious** (pär sə mō´ nē əs) *adj.* excessively thrifty; stingy
Ebenezer Scrooge was a *parsimonious* old man.
syn: cheap   *ant: extravagant*

15. **verbose** (vər bōs´) *adj.* using more words than are needed; wordy
Some find Charles Dickens so *verbose* that they swear he must have been paid by the word.
syn: prolix   .   *ant: terse; concise; succinct*

Exercise I

Words in Context

From the list below, supply the words needed to complete the paragraph. Some words will not be used.

odium	laudable	connived	verbose	befuddle
fallacy	noxious	chutzpah	crass	pandemonium

1. If the company representative had arrived a minute later, the crowd would have erupted into _____. Since discovering the hidden toxic dump behind a residential neighborhood, most of the residents felt nothing but _____ for Kraytron officials. The whole mess began just two weeks before, when children became ill from inhaling _____ vapors in the forest next to their development. Two days, one evacuation, and one hazardous material response team later, town officials declared the site to be an illegal dump for hazardous waste. Though a thorough investigation would take months, if not years, most of the town's residents immediately concluded that Kraytron officials must have _____ with a few greedy local officials in an effort to avoid the cost of waste disposal.

    When the booing and taunting finally stopped, the _____ Greg Haxton began his ninety-minute speech. Unknown to the public, Haxton had been Kraytron's unofficial crowd control specialist for over ten years.

    "Your concern for your environment is indeed _____," said Greg. "It's good to see a community that can pull together in a predicament." Greg continued with his positive observations for five minutes before coming to the reason for his speech. "I know that many of you are assuming that Kraytron created the dump because the factory is only two miles from the site. This rumor is a complete _____; the officials have already dated the site as being at least twenty years old—ten years before Kraytron even constructed the local facility. The dump can be attributed to the _____ decisions of the former Mattingdon Aluminum Mill officials; they ran the mill here for forty years before going bankrupt two decades ago. To those of you who are Kraytron employees, you must understand that Kraytron would never have the _____ to commit such a heinous crime against its own family."

From the list below, supply the words needed to complete the paragraph. Some words will not be used.

befuddle	liege	chutzpah	indiscreet
complacent	hypercritical	parsimonious	

2. "Come on, Jennifer, just buy a bag of charcoal! What are you going to save? Maybe a dime? I have never met a teenager as _____ as you."

    Silently mocking Julie, Jennifer grabbed the first bag of charcoal on the shelf. She knew that they were late for the cookout, but Julie's _____ attitude sometimes annoyed her. To Jennifer, it seemed as though Julie was always finding fault. They checked out at the register and walked to the car.

"I'm sorry if this _____ you," remarked Jennifer, "but as it stands, we're broke, which means that we need to watch our _____ spending. You've blown way too much money lately."

Julie didn't reply immediately; she just sat in the patchwork seat of the primer-colored subcompact with a[n] _____ look on her face. As Jennifer turned the key, she heard Julie mumble a facetious "Yes, my _____."

Exercise II

Sentence Completion

Complete the sentence in a way that shows you understand the meaning of the italicized vocabulary word.

1. Your *verbose* lecture is causing the audience to…

2. Complicated math problems always *befuddled* Gene, which is why he…

3. Though the apartment was immaculate, Lee's *hypercritical* mother still found…

4. The *liege* had only minutes to live, for the assassins were…

5. While working around *noxious* paint fumes, be sure to…

6. Leonard's *crass* demeanor sometimes caused Elmira to…

7. Though she was a millionaire, the *parsimonious* woman still…

8. The *complacent* security guard had no idea that…

9. The crooked commissioner *connived* with the mobster to…

10. The emergency planning committee has made a *laudable* effort to protect the city from…

11. Tawnya had the *chutzpah* to tell the speaker that…

12. Your *odium* for authority is only going to…

13. The *indiscreet* agent revealed his identity during…

14. Many people are guilty of believing the *fallacy* that…

15. *Pandemonium* ensued at the stadium when…

Exercise III

Roots, Prefixes, and Suffixes

Study the entries and answer the questions that follow.

The roots *loqu* and *locut* mean "speak, talk."
The roots *pend* and *pens* mean "hang."
The root *gest* means "carry" or "bring."
The suffix *–cy* means "the state or position of."
The prefix *e–* means "out."

1. Using *literal* translations as guidance, define the following words without using a dictionary:

A.	elocution	D.	pendant
B.	loquacious	E.	dependency
C.	eloquent	F.	gestation

2. The crowd eagerly awaited the _____ outcome of the horse race while the judges analyzed the photo finish.

3. A *gesture* is a motion of the body that is used to express or emphasize ideas or emotions. *Gesture* comes from the root *gest*, but how is the word related to this root?

4. List as many words as you can think of that contain the roots *loqu, locut,* and *gest*.

Exercise IV

Inference

Complete the sentences by inferring information about the italicized word from its context.

1. When the assembly instructions for a new appliance *befuddle* you, it is a good idea to…

2. If I am *hypercritical* while reviewing your work, and then you find a mistake in my work, you might tell me…

3. When your boss reads your *indiscreet* remarks about the company in tomorrow's paper, she will probably…

Exercise V

Writing

Here is a writing prompt similar to the one you will find on the writing portion of an assessment test.

Plan and write an essay based on the following statement:

> It was a high counsel that I once heard given to a young person, "Always do what you are afraid to do."
>
> –Ralph Waldo Emerson

Assignment: Write an essay in which you support or refute the above statement. Be certain to support your claim with evidence from literature, the arts, science and technology, current events, or your experience or observation.

Thesis: Write a *one-sentence* response to the above assignment. Make certain this single sentence offers a clear statement of your position.

Example: A person might accomplish great deeds, but never will if prevented by fear of failure.

_____

_____

Organizational Plan: List at least three subtopics you will use to support your main idea. This list is your outline.

1. _____

2. _____

3. _____

Draft: Following your outline, write a good first draft of your essay. Remember to support all your points with examples, facts, references to reading, etc.

Review and Revise: Exchange essays with a classmate. Using the scoring guide for Sentence Formation and Variety on page 260, score your partner's essay (while he or she scores yours). Focus on sentence structure and the use of language conventions. If necessary, rewrite your essay to improve the sentence structure and/or your use of language.

Exercise VI

Improving Paragraphs

Read the following passage and then choose the best revision for the underlined portions of the paragraph. The questions will require you to make decisions regarding the revision of the reading selection. Some revisions are not of actual mistakes, but will improve the clarity of the writing.

[1]

Those of you who <u>are intimidated</u>[1] by the prospect of analyzing fiction need not worry any longer. Analyzing fiction is like analyzing anything else. Everything you see in front of you is a text: your book, your desk, the pencil in your hand, the outdated schedule on the wall—even the room you're sitting in. There is a trick, be warned: To analyze something, you need to pay attention to the details. If you look at a <u>pencil, for example, and say, "a pencil,"</u>[2] then you're not going to accomplish much; however, if you look at a pencil and take note of the unevenly worn lead, the bite marks obscuring the "Number 2" marking, and the tiny dent in the metal band retaining the dirty <u>eraser; then you're</u>[3] starting to analyze.

1.   A. NO CHANGE
    B. is intimidated
    C. are intimidate
    D. is intimidation

2.   F. NO CHANGE
    G. pencil for example and say, "A pencil,"
    H. pencil, for example, and say, A Pencil"
    J. pencil, for example, and say, "A pencil,"

3.   A. NO CHANGE
    B. eraser, then you're
    C. eraser, then your
    D. eraser, than you're

[2]

(1)Once you note a few details that stand out, you can focus on one specific detail and apply some analytical questions to it: Why <u>is the lead worn unevenly.</u>[4] (2)Who uses this pencil? (3)What does this wear pattern tell me about the pencil? (4)<u>And, yes, this</u>[5] might feel like detective work, but that is how proper analysis of a text should feel, because what is a crime scene but another text to analyze? (5)You might also ask yourself what color the pencil is because most people assume that pencils are yellow, but there are obviously many more colors.

4.   F. NO CHANGE
    G. is the lead worn.
    H. is the lead worn unevenly?
    J. is the lead worn unevenly;

5.   A. NO CHANGE
    B. But yes, this
    C. No doubt this
    D. However,

[3]

The more time you spend on the details, the greater the chance becomes that you will find connections between two details. When you reach this point, you have yet another Focal Point[6] that can be used for analysis and discussion. Better yet. You might[7] find that the details somehow contradict each other. Contradictions literally beg you[8] for your thoughts—your theories as to why a detail or an element of a text is, indeed, a contradiction.

6. F. NO CHANGE
   G. Focal point
   H. focal Point
   J. focal point

7. A. NO CHANGE
   B. Better yet—You might
   C. Better yet, you might
   D. You, better yet, might

8. F. NO CHANGE
   G. practically beg you
   H. literally implore you
   J. especially try you

[4]

Contradictions, details that don't seem to belong in the text, and boring details that are so mundane that they seem entirely pointless,[9] are analytical gold. While analyzing a text, assume nothing is accidental—otherwise the author (painter, sculptor, creator, etc.) would not have bothered including it. If your text is a short story or a poem, then each and every word you read is there intentionally and has meaning. Why is the dried out earthworm mentioned by the author on the sidewalk?[10] Why does the protagonist wear a particular brand of shoes? These details are not there just to take up space—they have meaning. A detail might have meaning that is relevant to only one element of the text, but you will not know this until it's analyzed.[11]

9. A. NO CHANGE
   B. and mundane details that seem entirely pointless
   C. and boring, mundane details that seem pointless
   D. and details, boring and mundane, that seem entirely pointless

10. F. NO CHANGE
    G. Why is the dried-out earthworm on the sidewalk mentioned by the author?
    H. Why does the author mention the dried-out earthworm on the sidewalk?
    J. Why is the earthworm, dried out and on the sidewalk, mentioned by the author?

11. A. NO CHANGE
    B. the relevance until that specific detail is analyzed.
    C. it until it's analyzed.
    D. its relevance until the detail is analyzed.

[5]

There <u>are people who believe it or not spend</u>[12] weeks, months, or years of their lives researching the tiniest details in texts. These people are known as scholars, and they command the secret that befuddles so many students who can't seem to find a good topic for their term papers—that the smaller the topic is, the better. Find that footnote, or that one awkward word that doesn't seem to belong with the others. <u>There's the beginning of your topic.</u>[13] You can spend minutes or hours explaining what that single item means to the whole text. That one little word or phrase or object is a portal to a whole realm of study. The value of the prize, of course, depends on the student, but the ultimate prize is the insight that the research yields.

12. F. NO CHANGE
    G. are people who believe it or not spend
    H. are people who believe it, or not, spend
    J. are people who, believe it or not, spend

13. A. NO CHANGE
    B. There is the beginning of your topic.
    C. There's the beginning of your topic directly in front of you.
    D. There's the beginning of your topic:

14. Which sentence would be the most appropriate final sentence for the passage?
    F. If the student can assign a value to the dried-out earthworm, then he or she has a prize.
    G. The research done, if it provides insight into the earthworm, is well worth it and possibly entertaining, too.
    H. If the research yields even a single original insight into the text, then the effort is worth it and, perhaps, even interesting.
    J. So don't let literary analysis intimidate you; the more you simplify it, the more interesting it is.

15. If you had to delete an unnecessary or distracting sentence in paragraph 2, which one should it be?
    A. sentence 2
    B. sentence 3
    C. sentence 4
    D. sentence 5

Review Lessons 13-15

Exercise I

Inferences

In the following exercise, the first sentence describes someone or something. Infer information from the first sentence, and then choose the word from the Word Bank that best completes the second sentence.

acquitted	barrister	fallacy	juggernaut
liege	genial	obstreperous	parsimonious

1. Once she saw that it was, in fact, the cat that had ruined the tablet computer, Jen felt bad for having first blamed her son.

    From this sentence, we can infer that Jen _____ her son of ruining her computer.

2. So advanced was the alien technology that not even atomic weapons stopped them as they rampaged from one city to the next, destroying power plants, factories, and military bases.

    From this sentence, we can infer that the alien force was an unstoppable _____.

3. The miser reused things that most people simply threw in the trash, like plastic forks, foam cups, and, to everyone's disgust, paper napkins.

    From this sentence, we can infer that the _____ miser might not receive many dinner guests.

4. Business lags on days when Janine works the front desk because she is quick to become angry with customers.

    From this sentence, we can infer that the company should hire a more _____ person to deal with customers if it wants business to improve.

5. Because Ian had lost twelve straight games of rock-paper-scissors, he believed that he was due for a win, even though he had the same odds of winning with each new round.

    From this sentence, we can infer that Ian's notion that he is due to win is a[n] _____.

Exercise II

Related Words

Some of the vocabulary words from Lessons 13 through 15 have related meanings. Complete the following sentences by choosing the word that best fits the context, based on information you infer from the use of the italicized word. Some word pairs will be antonyms, some will be synonyms, and some will simply be words often used in the same context.

1. The _____ couple requested that wedding guests bring their own food to the reception, a proposal that even the most *frugal* of the invitees found appalling.
   A. bawdy
   B. parsimonious
   C. inert
   D. genial
   E. mundane

2. The *barrister* was good at her job, but still had compunctions when the courts _____ clients whom she suspected were, in fact, guilty.
   A. acquitted
   B. befuddled
   C. basked
   D. connived
   E. chastised

3. By claiming to be a real doctor, the _____ managed to *connive* thousands of people into buying her expensive vitamin supplements, which were no better than anything found in an ordinary grocery store.
   A. barrister
   B. hoax
   C. juggernaut
   D. novice
   E. charlatan

4. The _____ disease caused by the bacteria did not show *pernicious* effects until thirty years after the initial infection through a tick bite.
   A. nocturnal
   B. crass
   C. latent
   D. indiscreet
   E. verbose

5. *Myriad* fans swamped the football field in the _____ that ensued after the Super Bowl ended in a colossal upset.
   A. liege
   B. pandemonium
   C. adulation
   D. hoax
   E. levity

6. Jude considers still life paintings *mundane* unless the artist portrays some drama around the _____ objects, whether they happen to be fruit, flower vases, or bridges.
    A. inert
    B. amicable
    C. genial
    D. obstreperous
    E. frugal

7. Only the most *bawdy* nightclubs accepted the stand-up comedian known for his _____ humor, and even then, he was often chased off the stage by offended audiences.
    A. fickle
    B. marital
    C. crass
    D. laudable
    E. artful

8. The _____ traveler could strike up conversations with even the weariest of strangers and fill them with *jocose* laughter in a matter of minutes.
    A. bawdy
    B. culinary
    C. fickle
    D. genial
    E. naïve

9. The *hypercritical* manager _____ his subordinates, demanding they use his methods even if the employees had found better ways of getting the job done.
    A. basked
    B. chastised
    C. circumvented
    D. acquitted
    E. befuddled

10. The _____ thief had an easy day of work picking the pockets of *naïve* tourists who were paying more attention to the Thanksgiving Day parade than to their own wallets, watches, and purses.
    A. frugal
    B. inert
    C. artful
    D. latent
    E. fickle

Exercise III

Deeper Meanings

Choose a word to replace the italicized word in each sentence. All of the possible choices for each sentence have similar definitions, but the correct answer will have a connotation that best suits the context. For example, the words "delete," "destroy," and "obliterate" all mean "to remove or wipe out," but no one would ever say, "I destroyed the name from the document." The correct choice will be the word that has the best specific meaning and does not render the sentence awkward in tone or content. When choices seem close, look for a clue in the context that makes one choice better than the other.

Note that the correct answer is not always the primary vocabulary word from the lesson.

thrilled	economical	pleased	discomfort	overjoyed
dirty	odium	bawdy	cheap	con artist
ecstatic	phony	dislike		

1. Bo received an after school detention for using *rude* language during an anatomy lesson in health class, in spite of his teacher's warning before class that such jokes would not be tolerated.

    Better word: _____

2. Bringing your own dessert to a restaurant in order to save money is not just *frugal*—it's an insult to the restaurant owner.

    Better word: _____

3. Mike felt like a[n] *charlatan* because he had said he could dance, but he had lied.

    Better word: _____

4. Jan was *enraptured* to announce that grilled cheese would replace the equally mundane turkey slices served in the cafeteria on Thursdays.

    Better word: _____

5. The owners of the waste landfill had, indeed, created many jobs and improved the local roads, but even that didn't ease the *annoyance* felt by the nearest residents, who lost their nice view, fresh air, and property values.

    Better word: _____

Exercise IV

Crossword Puzzle

Use the clues to complete the crossword puzzle. The answers consist of vocabulary words from Lessons 13 through 15.

Across

2. like a barrel of toxic waste
4. untruth
5. dumb and happy
7. take a hot bath?
10. like a penny pincher
11. like an armored T-Rex
15. likely to offend
16. gifted with gab
17. business as usual

Down

1. phony pro
3. going nowhere
6. get around
7. your friend in a court
8. boss in the castle
9. dealing with good taste
12. many
13. sleeps during the day
14. a rookie

Exercise V

Subject Prompts

Here is a writing prompt similar to the one you will find on the writing portion of an assessment test. Follow the instructions below and write a brief, efficient essay.

> The Age of Information has brought countless advancements, perhaps, but it also guarantees individuals a digital history, which might not be a good thing. Imagine interviewing for a high-powered job one day only to be turned down because your prospective employers find pictures of you being foolish on your social networking page, or read comments you made on a political website. The things you have posted online are there forever, or must be assumed to be permanent since you have no control over what people do with data you post, even if that means simply leaving it posted for eternity.
>
> What do you recommend to friends who express interest in posting pictures or text, publically, on the Internet? How would you advocate it or condemn it? Include at least three reasons why you do or do not support it.

Thesis: Write a *one-sentence* response to the above assignment. Make certain this single sentence offers a clear statement of your position.

Example: Images or personal data should never be posted on public Internet sites because they may be seen by and judged negatively by someone.

_____

_____

Organizational Plan: List at least three subtopics you will use to support your main idea. This list is your outline.

1. _____

2. _____

3. _____

Draft: Following your outline, write a good first draft of your essay. Remember to support all your points with examples, facts, references to reading, etc.

Review and Revise: Exchange essays with a classmate. Using the Holistic scoring guide on page 262, score your partner's essay (while he or she scores yours). If necessary, rewrite your essay to correct the problems noted by your partner.

Lesson Sixteen

1. **purloin** (pər loin´) *v.* to steal
    They had not planned to *purloin* the jewels, but the temptation was too great.
    syn: burglarize

2. **linguistics** (ling wis´ tiks) *n.* the scientific study of the structure, sounds, and meaning of language
    The professor of *linguistics* explained how English evolved from a number of other languages.

3. **pique** (pēk) *v.* to cause resentment; to provoke
    The old gentleman was *piqued* because he was not given a seat at the head table.
    syn: irritate   *ant: assuage*

4. **rabid** (rab´ id) *adj.* raging; fanatical
    After working out, Chrissy had a *rabid* thirst and drank two gallons of water.
    syn: uncontrollable; fervid   *ant: placid*

5. **precocious** (pri kō´ shəs) *adj.* showing early development, especially mental
    Anthony was such a *precocious* three-year-old that he could already play the violin well.
    syn: advanced

6. **predatory** (pred´ ə tôr ē) *adj.* inclined to prey on others
    The buzzard is a scavenger, but the hawk is a *predatory* animal.
    syn: pillaging; despoiling   *ant: nurturing*

7. **plebeian** (pli bē´ ən) *n.* a commoner; one from the lower class
                                         adj. common or vulgar
    (*n.*) Seniors treated the freshmen as though they were *plebeians*.
    (*adj.*) The baroness refused to do the *plebeian* chores of cooking and cleaning.
    (*n.*) *syn: peon; peasant*   *ant: liege*
    (*adj.*) *syn: base; lowly*   *ant: refined; aristocratic*

8. **pugnacious** (pug nā´ shəs) *adj.* eager and ready to fight; quarrelsome
    Because he was so *pugnacious*, he had few friends.
    syn: combative; belligerent   *ant: placid; pacific*

9. **prowess** (prow´ is) *n.* superior skill or ability
    Ty's physical *prowess* was matched by his superior mental ability.
    syn: strength; dominance; power   *ant: weakness*

10. **pusillanimous** (pyōō sə lan′ ə məs) *adj.* cowardly; fearful
The Wizard of Oz granted the *pusillanimous* lion his wish to have courage.
syn: fainthearted; timid *ant: brave; bold*

11. **vindictive** (vin dik′ tiv) *adj.* seeking revenge; bearing a grudge
Out of some *vindictive* urge, Steve slashed his ex-girlfriend's tires.
syn: vengeful *ant: forgiving*

12. **quell** (kwel) *v.* to put an end to; to allay or quiet
The police were called in to *quell* the riot.
syn: calm *ant: foment; incite*

13. **rabble** (rab′ əl) *n.* a disorderly crowd, a mob
The guards had to protect the president from the *rabble* in the streets.
syn: riffraff

14. **raconteur** (rak on tər′) *n.* a person skilled at telling stories
An exceptional *raconteur*, Lorna held the whole audience spellbound with her stories.

15. **quixotic** (kwik sot′ ik) *adj.* very idealistic; impractical; caught up in romantic notions
As a young man, he had the *quixotic* notion that he could single-handedly end poverty in the country.

Exercise I

Words in Context

From the list below, supply the words needed to complete the paragraph. Some words will not be used.

quell	linguistics	vindictive	rabble
prowess	purloin	pugnacious	

1. "Your _____ on the field does not excuse your _____ behavior at school. This is the second time that you've been in trouble for fighting," said the principal. She hated this situation; she knew what to do, but in the way the school perceived her, it would be a lose-lose decision. Punishing Isaac before the district championship game would surely draw a[n] _____ of angry students and parents to her office. Being lenient with Isaac would fuel the already _____ attitudes of second-offenders throughout the school. The turbulent aftermath of either decision would be difficult to _____.

From the list below, supply the words needed to complete the paragraph. Some words will not be used.

plebeian	pique	raconteur	quell
linguistics	precocious		

2. Everyone had high hopes for the _____ youngster. At the age of six, Mariah seemed to have such a command of _____ that a simple conversation with her might easily arouse anger and _____ in even the brightest of her classmates; consequently, they felt as though they were speaking to an adult, rather than to a child. She also loved to exercise her fine speaking abilities. Never at a loss for words, the young _____ would come home from school every night and vividly describe the events of her day to her parents.

From the list below, supply the words needed to complete the paragraph. Some words will not be used.

plebeian	quixotic	linguistics	pusillanimous
predatory	rabid	purloin	

3. Owing in part to his _____ interest in the heroic tales of Arthur's knights set in the Middle Ages, Delmar had a rather _____ perspective of the world. He never simply "went to work" or "picked up a burger at the drive-through"; instead, Delmar lived in a fantasy world in which each day he had to uphold his chivalric duty while challenging a myriad of perilous obstacles. The pigeons on the roof of his apartment were not pigeons—they were great, _____ winged beasts, perpetually waiting to swoop down and _____ Delmar's poppyseed bagel as he walked to his chariot—a rusty Ford Granada that had recently passed the two hundred thousand-mile mark. After a short ride to the Hall of Lords (the metro station), Delmar would spend the day protecting the ignorant _____ from microscopic legions of evil warriors, mainly by spraying all surfaces with disinfectant before wiping them down with a rag. Evil dirt warriors were not Delmar's greatest problem; sometimes he had to confront the mystical rat-beasts that lived in the basement storage area. Indeed, the basement was no place for _____ folk—only knights as brave as Sir Delmar.

Exercise II

Sentence Completion

Complete the sentence in a way that shows you understand the meaning of the italicized vocabulary word.

1. Let's see if your *prowess* during practice extends to the…

2. The dressmaker *piqued* Linda by pointing out that she…

3. The tear gas easily *quelled* the protestors at…

4. The filthy tavern was full of *pugnacious* characters looking for…

5. Everyone knew that Colt was too *pusillanimous* to ever become a professional…

6. The new *linguistics* teacher claimed that writing was just as important as…

7. The *precocious* preschooler was already good at…

8. After three days of surviving in the wilderness, the co-pilot's *rabid* hunger drove her to…

9. The audience was engrossed with the old *raconteur's* accounts of…

10. The *rabble* outside the governor's mansion chanted about the new policy on…

11. Still *vindictive* about losing the promotion to a younger associate, Elvira made life…

12. After he *purloined* the company secrets, Sol went to the competition and…

13. The *quixotic* Dexter thought that he alone could someday…

14. Carnivorous *predatory* animals will eat meat before they will eat…

15. The greedy Duke never responded to the *plebeian* requests for…

Exercise III

Roots, Prefixes, and Suffixes

Study the entries and answer the questions that follow.

The root *man* means "hand."
The suffix *–escent* means "becoming."
The roots *nat* and *nas* mean "born."
The prefix *in–* means "in."
The prefix *re–* means "again."

1. Using *literal* translations as guidance, define the following words without using a dictionary:

   A. manacles
   B. innate
   C. nativity
   D. nascent
   E. renascence
   F. manicure

2. Literally, *manual labor* is labor _____.
   The word *manufacture* contains two roots: _____ and _____. It literally means _____.
   Manipulation literally refers to _____, and the word *manuscript* literally means _____.

3. A *mandate* is an order or a command. How do you think this word got its meaning?

4. List all the words you can think of that have the suffix *–escent*.

5. List all the words that you can think of that contain the roots *nat* or *nas*.

Exercise IV

Inference

Complete the sentences by inferring information about the italicized word from its context.

1. Geoff is very *pugnacious*, so if someone accidentally spills a beverage on him, he will probably...

2. If the police are sent to *quell* a riot, they might...

3. Gwendolyn and the Duke of Trombonia loved each other, but since Gwendolyn was a *plebeian*, they...

Exercise V

Critical Reading

Below is a pair of reading passages followed by several multiple-choice questions. Carefully read the passages and choose the best answer for each of the questions.

These two passages, written by authors separated by two centuries, address the topic of learning. Francis Bacon wrote "Of Studies" in 1625 as part of the collection, The Essays or Counsels, Civil and Moral. *Passage 2 is an adapted except of a lecture, "On the Elevation of the Laboring Classes," by William Ellery Channing, 1840.*

Passage 1

STUDIES serve for delight, for ornament, and for ability. Their chief use for delight, is in privateness and retiring; for ornament, is in discourse; and for ability, is in the judgment, and disposition of business. For expert men can execute, and perhaps judge of particulars, one by one; but the general counsels, and the plots and marshalling of affairs, come best, from those that
5   are learned. To spend too much time in studies is sloth; to use them too much for ornament, is affectation; to make judgment wholly by their rules, is the humor of a scholar. They perfect nature, and are perfected by experience: for natural abilities are like natural plants, that need pruning, by study; and studies themselves, do give forth directions too much at large, except they be bounded in by experience. Crafty men scorn studies, simple men admire them, and wise men
10   use them; for they teach not their own use; but that is a wisdom without them, and above them, won by observation. Read not to contradict and confute; nor to believe and take for granted; nor to find talk and discourse; but to weigh and consider. Some books are to be tasted, others to be swallowed, and some few to be chewed and digested; that is, some books are to be read only in parts; others to be read, but not curiously; and some few to be read wholly, and with diligence
15   and attention. Some books also may be read by deputy, and extracts made of them by others; but that would be only in the less important arguments, and the meaner sort of books, else distilled books are like common distilled waters, flashy things. Reading maketh a full man; conference a ready man; and writing an exact man. And therefore, if a man write little, he had need have a great memory; if he confer little, he had need have a present wit: and if he read little, he had need
20   have much cunning, to seem to know, that he doth not. Histories make men wise; poets witty; the mathematics exceptional; natural philosophy deep; moral grave; logic and rhetoric able to contend. *Abeunt studia in mores* [studies become character]. Nay, there is no post or impediment in the wit, but may be wrought out by fit studies; like as diseases of the body, may have appropriate exercises. Bowling is good for the stone and reins; shooting for the lungs and breast; gentle
25   walking for the stomach; riding for the head; and the like. So if a man's wit be wandering, let him study the mathematics; for in demonstrations, if his wit be called away never so little, he must begin again. If his wit be not apt to distinguish or find differences, let him study the Schoolmen; for they are *cymini sectores* [hair splitters]. If he be not apt to beat over matters, and to call up one thing to prove and illustrate another, let him study the lawyers' cases. So every defect of the mind,
30   may have a special receipt.

Passage 2

Undoubtedly some men are more gifted than others, and are marked out for more studious lives. But the work of such men is not to do others' thinking for them, but to help them to think more vigorously and effectually. Great minds are to make others great. Their superiority is to be used, not to break the multitude to intellectual vassalage, not to establish over them a spiritual
5 tyranny, but to rouse them from lethargy, and to aid them to judge for themselves. The light and life which spring up in one soul are to be spread far and wide. Of all treasons against humanity, there is no one worse than his who employs great intellectual force to keep down the intellect of his less favored brother.

It is sometimes urged by those who consider the multitude as not intended to think, that
10 at best they can learn but little, and that this is likely to harm rather than to do them good. "A little learning," we are told, "is a dangerous thing." "Shallow draughts" of knowledge are worse than ignorance. The mass of the people, it is said, can go to the bottom of nothing; and the result of stimulating them to thought will be the formation of a dangerous set of half-thinkers. To this argument I reply, first, that it has the inconvenience of proving too much; for, if valid, it shows
15 that none of any class ought to think. For who, I would ask, can go to the bottom of anything? Whose "learning" is not "little"? Whose "draughts" of knowledge are not "shallow"? Who of us has fathomed the depths of a single product of nature or a single event in history? Who of us is not baffled by the mysteries in a grain of sand? How contracted the range of the widest intellect! But is our knowledge, because so little, of no worth? Are we to despise the lessons which are taught us
20 in this nook of creation, in this narrow round of human experience, because an infinite universe stretches around us, which we have no means of exploring, and in which the earth, and sun, and planets dwindle to a point? We should remember that the known, however little it may be, is in harmony with the boundless unknown, and a step towards it. We should remember, too, that the gravest truths may be gathered from a very narrow compass of information. God is revealed in his
25 smallest work as truly as in his greatest. The principles of human nature may be studied better in a family than in the history of the world. The finite is a manifestation of the infinite. The great ideas, of which I have formerly spoken, are within the reach of every man who thirsts for truth, and seeks it with singleness of mind. I will only add, that the laboring class is not now condemned to draughts of knowledge so shallow as to merit scorn. Many of them know more of the outward
30 world than all the philosophers of antiquity; and Christianity has opened to them mysteries of the spiritual world which kings and prophets were not privileged to understand. And are they, then, to be doomed to spiritual inaction, as incapable of useful thought?

1. Which of the following choices is *not* among the purpose of studies, according to passage 1, lines 1-5?
   A. fun
   B. making decisions
   C. politics
   D. resting
   E. doing business

2A. Studies provide *ornament* to be used for which one of the following activities, according to passage 1?
  A. graduating
  B. communicating
  C. promotion
  D. learning
  E. business

2B. As it is used in passage 1, line 6, *affectation* most nearly means
  A. showing off.
  B. being heroic.
  C. well done.
  D. considerate.
  E. condemnable.

3. Line 11 from passage 1 advises to "read not to contradict and confute," which suggests that
  A. reading can be used to show intellectualism.
  B. assistance should be sought with the subject.
  C. one should study with pure motives.
  D. lectures are more effective for revenge.
  E. one should believe anything in print.

4A. "Shallow draught" alludes to a famous quotation from an Alexander Pope essay: "Drink deep, or taste not the Pierian spring; there shallow draughts intoxicate the brain." In the context of the metaphor as it is used in passage 2, the "water" refers to
  A. religion.
  B. the mind.
  C. hardship.
  D. knowledge.
  E. humanity.

4B. Who, according to the author of passage 2, has a "shallow draught" of knowledge?
  A. the new former nobility
  B. the upper classes
  C. the laborers
  D. the modern clergy
  E. the population in general

5A. The author of passage 2 makes an accusation in the introductory paragraph against any person who would
  A. claim superior intelligence over others.
  B. attempt to recruit other intellectuals.
  C. use his own knowledge to hinder the intellect of others.
  D. assign more importance to studies than to the soul.
  E. use their superior intellects for the advancement of others.

5B. As used in line 4, passage 2, *vassalage* most nearly means
    A.   superiority.
    B.   thought.
    C.   autonomy.
    D.   work.
    E.   servitude.

6.   Choose the statement that best rephrases the following quotation from passage 2.

"...the laboring class is not now condemned to draughts of knowledge so shallow as to merit scorn."

    A.   The working class is free to learn as much as it desires.
    B.   The laborers may learn, but only in a small amount.
    C.   Those among the working class will be punished if caught learning.
    D.   The workers should scorn their own shallow knowledge.
    E.   Laborers are no longer captives on prison ships for their knowledge.

7A. Which choice best describes the intent of passage 1?
    A.   argument
    B.   biography
    C.   entertainment
    D.   instruction
    E.   humor

7B. Choose the best description of the organizational style of passage 1.
    A.   cause and effect
    B.   compare and contrast
    C.   how-to
    D.   pros and cons
    E.   chronological

8A. Passage 2, unlike passage 1, is intended to
    A.   inform.
    B.   persuade.
    C.   catalog.
    D.   restate.
    E.   teach.

8B. Which one of the following types of content in passage 2 *least contributes* to your answer to question 8A?
    A.   judgmental language to describe enemies of the cause
    B.   the use of *we* to include the audience in the author's argument
    C.   positive portrayals of the newly learning population
    D.   the rare use of compound sentences
    E.   responses to arguments contrary to the author's cause

9A. Choose the statement that successfully rephrases the following sentence from passage 2.

"We should remember that the known, however little it may be, is in harmony with the boundless unknown, and a step towards it."

    A.   Each new thing learned will reveal that it is virtually no gain.
    B.   The limits of knowledge coincide with the books available.
    C.   Be warned that boundless knowledge is unknown territory.
    D.   All knowledge is good knowledge and will help you to understand more.
    E.   When learning approaches the boundaries of knowledge, it is unknown.

9B. The authors of both passages would agree that
    A.   knowledge should be limited to the upper class.
    B.   intellect has many levels of value.
    C.   knowledge does not change people.
    D.   the working class can learn, but not as much as scholars can.
    E.   knowledge has limits, though they might require a lifetime to reach.

10A. While the author of passage 2 simply wants the masses to read and learn, the author of passage 1 is concerned more about
    A.   the religious alignment of the books.
    B.   the specific technique with which certain books are read.
    C.   the source of the books and their subject areas.
    D.   assisting the lower social classes with education.
    E.   discussing travel and literature.

10B. Choose the quotation from passage 1 that best supports your answer to question 10A.
    A.   "Reading maketh a full man; conference a ready man; and writing an exact man."
    B.   "…distilled books are like common distilled waters…"
    C.   "Some books are to be tasted, others to be swallowed, and some few to be chewed and digested…"
    D.   "Crafty men scorn studies, simple men admire them…"
    E.   "Histories make men wise; poets witty; the mathematics exceptional…"

Vocabulary Power Plus for College and Career Readiness

LEVEL TEN

Lesson Seventeen

1. **repose** (ri pōz´) *n.* a state of relaxation or sleep
   After an extremely difficult work week, Martin spent the weekend in *repose*.
   syn: respite; peace   *ant: distress; agitation*

2. **caustic** (kô´ stik) *adj.* biting; stingingly sharp or sarcastic; highly irritating
   Because of his *caustic* comments, his wife finally left him.
   syn: acidic; harsh   *ant: mild; pleasant*

3. **exodus** (ek´ sə dəs) *n.* a mass departure or emigration
   The many defeated tribes made a speedy *exodus* from the war-torn valley.
        ant: return

4. **retribution** (ret rə byōō´ shən) *n.* something justly deserved, especially a punishment
   The boys had to spend the weekend picking up litter in *retribution* for having spray-painted graffiti on the bus.
   syn: reprisal   *ant: reward*

5. **abscond** (ab skond´) *v.* to depart quickly and secretly, especially to avoid punishment
   The shoplifter *absconded* with a stack of video games, only to find the store's security waiting for him in the parking lot.
   syn: flee; bolt   *ant: remain; stay*

6. **raillery** (rā´ lə rē) *n.* good-humored ridicule or teasing
   James much prefers Carson's *raillery* to the cynical slurs of other comedians.
   syn: banter

7. **scourge** (skûrj) *n.* a person or thing that causes great trouble or misfortune
   Cancer remains one of the worst *scourges* of mankind.
   syn: torment; bane; curse   *ant: boon; blessing*

8. **agnostic** (ag nos´ tik) *adj.* believing in neither side of an argument
   Since he was new to the area, Jim stayed *agnostic* in matters of local politics, at least until he learned more.
   syn: questioning; ambivalent   *ant: devoted*

9. **terse** (tûrs) *adj.* brief and to the point
   Julia didn't give me any details about her break-up, just a *terse* "it's over."
   syn: abbreviated; curt   *ant: verbose; rambling*

10. **circumspect** (sûr´ kəm spekt) *adj.*   careful; heedful; attentive to all points
    Although I tried to be *circumspect* about my friends, I never guessed that one of them had a criminal record.
    syn: judicious; prudent   *ant: rash; foolhardy*

11. **uncanny** (un kan´ ē) *adj.*   weird; strange; so keen or acute as to seem bizarre
    Tess had an *uncanny* memory for details; she knew exactly what she had worn on any given day in the past eleven years.
    syn: eerie

12. **penitent** (pen´ i tənt) *adj.*   remorseful; sorry for having done wrong
    Seeing the boy's *penitent* expression, the judge was easier on him than he might otherwise have been.
    syn: apologetic   *ant: unrepentant*

13. **vindicate** (vin´ di kāt) *v.*   to clear of suspicion or accusations
    Darren sued for libel in order to *vindicate* his reputation.
    syn: exonerate; acquit   *ant: besmirch; implicate*

14. **renegade** (ren´ i gād) *n.*   one who deserts one side in favor of another; traitor; outlaw
    The members of the old party called him a *renegade*; the members of his new party called him a patriot.
    syn: turncoat; defector   *ant: loyalist*

15. **taciturn** (tas´ i tûrn) *adj.*   not fond of talking; usually silent
    We were amazed when the *taciturn* young man signed up for public speaking.
    syn: reticent; reserved   *ant: garrulous; loquacious;*
                                                                 talkative

Exercise I

Words in Context

From the list below, supply the words needed to complete the paragraph. Some words will not be used.

| penitent | abscond | agnostic | scourge | circumspect |
| retribution | repose | exodus | | |

1. Sergeant Neil Newman, one of six mine removal experts in Southeast Asia, makes sure that he is _____ about every aspect of his job.

    "There is _____ for mistakes in this line of work, no doubt," warns Newman. "If you take a little mental _____ while you're on the job, and overlook a tripwire, for example, then you'll be lucky to _____ with your life. You can't outrun high explosives. You won't have the chance to be _____ about your error."

    The uncharted minefields that Neil faces have been a[n] _____ on war-torn nations for decades, and experts estimate that it will take people like Neil hundreds of years to find and neutralize the millions of underground threats.

From the list below, supply the words needed to complete the paragraph. Some words will not be used.

| raillery | vindicate | terse | taciturn |
| abscond | uncanny | exodus | renegade |

2. The _____ Haley silently stared at her console despite the elated atmosphere of the command center. While everyone celebrated the latest victory of the rebel forces, Haley received a message that would soon turn the celebration into panic. Two _____ had revealed the secret location of the command center, and as soon as she gave the word, the entire facility would have to prepare for a[n] _____ to a new location before the Nationalist forces arrived. The Nationalists had a[n] _____ ability to turn the rebels against each other; this would be the third time in three months that the rebels were forced to relocate their base of operations. Haley took a breath, swiveled around in her chair, and prepared to deliver a[n] _____ briefing that would squelch the group's cheerful air. To make matters worse, one of the traitors turned out to be Haley's cousin, a lieutenant whom Haley recently helped _____ from espionage charges.

From the list below, supply the words needed to complete the paragraph. Some words will not be used.

| terse | raillery | caustic | agnostic | scourge |

3. Paige and Mia have been friends for more than twenty years, despite the fact that Paige is devoutly religious and Mia is _____. They often have heated discussions about religion, but their conversation inevitably turns into good-humored _____. Over the years, they learned to avoid making _____ comments during an argument, no matter how angry they might get.

Exercise II

Sentence Completion

Complete the sentence in a way that shows you understand the meaning of the italicized vocabulary word.

1. The maniacal dictator was a *scourge* on mankind until…

2. The victims of the bombing demanded *retribution* for their…

3. Sheila's *caustic* tongue made her supervisor think twice about…

4. The acrobatic trio had the *uncanny* ability to…

5. A little *repose* is necessary for…

6. Urik's family finally *vindicated* him after he spent eight years in prison for…

7. Though his parents were bothered by it, Thomas remained *agnostic* in…

8. Leif knew who had *absconded* with his popcorn because…

9. The *renegade* mercenary quietly left his platoon in order to…

10. The *circumspect* fashion designer made sure the dress…

11. Major Buchanan gave a *terse* briefing about the invading squadron of…

12. Good humored *raillery* did not please the new teacher, who in turn…

13. As the last stone was removed from the cave entrance, an *exodus* of…

14. The *taciturn* Willow surprised everyone when she decided to become…

15. The *penitent* fugitive decided to stop running and…

Exercise III

Roots, Prefixes, and Suffixes

Study the entries and answer the questions that follow.

The root *phil* means "love" or "loving."
The root *ocul* means "eye."
The root *mar* means "sea."
The prefix *sub–* means "under."

1. Using *literal* translations as guidance, define the following words without using a dictionary:

    A. philanthropy   D. ocular
    B. philharmonic   E. oculist
    C. maritime   F. submarine

2. The root *sophos* means "wise," so a *philosopher* is one who _____

    _____.

    The root *moros* means "foolish" or "fool"; therefore, the literal meaning of *sophomore* is _____.

3. *Phile* is sometimes found at the end of a word. What do you suppose the following people love?

    anglophiles:
    francophiles:
    bibliophiles:

4. List all the words you can think of that contain the roots *phil*, *ocul* or *mar*.

Exercise IV

Inference

Complete the sentences by inferring information about the italicized word from its context.

1. The pianist didn't even need an electronic tuner; she had the *uncanny* ability to…

2. If Mr. Reckner cannot *vindicate* himself from the charges of grand larceny, he will probably…

3. Damian, who went to school despite the fact that he was sick with influenza, became the *scourge* of his class when…

Exercise V

Writing

Here is a writing prompt similar to the one you will find on the writing portion of an assessment test.

Plan and write an essay based on the following statement:

> Genius is a strange, intangible force. It is an indefinable, peculiar something that possesses a certain class of extraordinary human beings and gives vent to itself in a manner that impresses and confounds mortals.
>
> –Elwood S. Brown, The Promoter; His Genius
> From *Clever Business Sketches* (1909)

Assignment: In an essay, discuss the merit of Brown's appraisal of genius. Use evidence from your reading, your studies, your observations, and your experience to support your opinion.

Thesis: Write a *one-sentence* response to the above assignment. Make certain this single sentence offers a clear statement of your position.

Example: Elwood Brown labels geniuses as impressive and confounding, but his failure to describe an actual genius leaves too many open questions to make his definition valid.

_____

_____

Organizational Plan: List at least three subtopics you will use to support your main idea. This list is your outline.

1. _____

2. _____

3. _____

Draft: Following your outline, write a good first draft of your essay. Remember to support all your points with examples, facts, references to reading, etc.

Review and Revise: Exchange essays with a classmate. Using the scoring guide for Word Choice on page 261, score your partner's essay (while he or she scores yours). Focus on word choice and the use of language conventions. If necessary, rewrite your essay to improve word choice and/or your use of language.

Exercise VI

English Practice

Identifying Sentence Errors

Identify the grammatical error in each of the following sentences. If the sentence contains no error, select answer choice E.

1. When the warden <u>agreed to us</u> that the prisoner <u>should be released</u>, we
                 (A)   (B)
    <u>were pleased to accept</u> the <u>invitation</u> <u>to the parole hearing</u>.   <u>No error</u>
           (C)   (D)   (E)

2. The <u>new park project</u> <u>for underprivileged</u> children <u>was began</u> in the
             (A)   (B)   (C)
    spring but <u>will not be completed</u> until late November.   <u>No error</u>
                 (D)   (E)

3. <u>Last year, we had</u> an especially severe winter, and <u>despite our efforts</u> to
       (A)   (B)
    remove the snow, it <u>had lain</u> on the barn roof <u>all season</u>.   <u>No error</u>
                    (C)   (D)   (E)

4. When all the <u>votes are</u> in and <u>are counted</u>, <u>it alone</u> will decide
                  (A)   (B)   (C)
    <u>the next governor</u> of this fine state.   <u>No error</u>
        (D)   (E)

5. The speaker at the horse-breeders' convention <u>would have been</u> better if she
                                                  (A)
    <u>took the time</u> <u>to prepare</u> for the subjects of interest <u>to the audience</u>.   <u>No error</u>
       (B)   (C)   (D)   (E)

Improving Sentences

The underlined portion of each sentence below contains some flaw. Select the answer choice that best corrects the flaw.

6. The aging movie star was particular about her appearance and <u>was as particularly engaging as ever</u> when she looked her best.
    A. was as particular as engaging as ever
    B. was as engaging particularly as ever
    C. was as ever particularly engaging
    D. was as engaging as ever
    E. was particularly engaging

7. We were bouncing a basketball in the driveway, and a neighbor came over and told us we were making too much noise.
   A. When we were bouncing a basketball in the driveway, a neighbor came over to tell us we were making too much noise.
   B. A neighbor came over to tell us we were making too much noise and we were bouncing a basketball in the driveway.
   C. We were bouncing a basketball when a neighbor in the driveway came over to tell us we were making too much noise.
   D. Bouncing a basketball, a neighbor came over and told us we were making too much noise in the driveway.
   E. When a neighbor came over and told us to bounce a basketball in the driveway, we were making too much noise.

8. Hoping for the support of his constituents was the incumbent candidate who ran against a strong opponent for the position of state senator.
   A. One incumbent state senator candidate ran against a strong opponent and hoped for his constituents' support.
   B. Hoping his constituents would support him, the incumbent candidate for state senator faced a strong opponent.
   C. Running against a strong opponent was an incumbent state senator candidate who hoped for the constituent support.
   D. Hoping to be state senator the incumbent candidate ran against a strong opponent and was hoping for the support of his constituents.
   E. The incumbent candidate was hoping for the support of his constituents when running against a strong opponent for state-senator.

9. Alfred was able to secure a government job after he graduated from college which lasted for almost twenty years.
   A. Alfred lasted almost twenty years after he was able to secure a government job after he graduated from college.
   B. After he graduated from college which lasted for almost twenty years, Alfred was able to secure a government job.
   C. Alfred was able to graduate from college to secure a government job which lasted for almost twenty years.
   D. After graduating from college, Alfred was able to secure a government job that lasted for almost twenty years.
   E. For almost twenty years, Alfred was able to secure a government job after he graduated from college.

10. When children play in the street without any shoes and their mothers know about it and the neighbors don't tell them to stop.
    A. Children don't tell their neighbors to stop when they play in the street without shoes and their mothers know about it.
    B. When the children play without any shoes in the street, and their mothers know about it, the neighbors don't stop them from playing.
    C. When neighbors don't tell them to stop, children play in the street without any shoes and their mothers know about it.
    D. Without shoes, children play in the street and their mothers know about it and the neighbors don't tell them to stop.
    E. Their mothers know about it and children play in the street without shoes and the neighbors don't tell them to stop.

Lesson Eighteen

1. **xenophobia** (ze nə fō´ bē ə) *n.* an intense dislike or fear of strangers or foreigners
   Tim's *xenophobia* gave him an unwarranted hatred for immigrants coming to America.

2. **irreverent** (i rev´ rənt) *adj.* disrespectful
   John's *irreverent* attitude toward his pastor embarrassed and angered his mother.
   syn: insubordinate   *ant: worshipful*

3. **discordant** (dis kōrd´ dənt) *adj.* being in disagreement
   The angry and *discordant* voices echoed throughout the conference room.
   syn: conflicting   *ant: harmonious*

4. **torpid** (tōr´ ped) *adj.* losing motion, feeling, or power; lacking in energy
   The sleeping gas caused the hero's mind to become *torpid*.
   syn: apathetic; lethargic   *ant: energetic*

5. **filibuster** (fil´ ə bəs tər) *v.* to attempt to block a bill from becoming law by
   speaking at length against it
   The Senator from Mississippi gave an eight-hour speech to *filibuster* the new tax bill.
   syn: derail

6. **subjugate** (sub´ ji gāt) *v.* to dominate, conquer, or bring under control
   The invaders *subjugated* the natives and forced them to do manual labor.
   syn: repress   *ant: free*

7. **inherent** (in hir´ ənt) *adj.* essential
   Emissions causing air pollution is the major *inherent* drawback of the automobile.
   syn: intrinsic   *ant: extrinsic; extraneous*

8. **pristine** (pris´ tēn) *adj.* pure; completely clean and uncontaminated
   The vast, pristine wilderness of northern Alaska is too cold and remote for most
   people to inhabit.
   syn: pure   *ant: defiled; spoiled; sullied*

9. **invective** (in vek´ tiv) *n.* an insult or abuse in speech
   Scott's *invective*, aimed at his teacher, resulted in an immediate trip to the principal's
   office.
   syn: reproach   *ant: praise*

10. **impregnable** (im preg´ nə bəl) *adj.* not able to be conquered; impenetrable
    The Greek warriors were unable to conquer the *impregnable* Trojan fortress.
    syn: unbeatable   *ant: vulnerable*

11. **expedite** (ek´ spə dīt) *v.* to increase the rate of progress
More construction workers were brought on to the project to help *expedite* the construction of the new bridge.
syn: hurry; hasten; streamline   *ant: retard; hinder*

12. **prodigal** (prä´ di gəl) *adj.* reckless, wasteful, and extravagant
The *prodigal* actor was notorious for his lavish, excessive, and unruly lifestyle.
syn: wastrel; libertine   *ant: prudent*

13. **subdued** (sub dōōd´) *adj.* reduced in strength, tone, or manner
The spy wore *subdued* colors in order to blend in with the crowd.
syn: restrained; solemn   *ant: bright; excited*

14. **tenuous** (ten´ yə wəs) *adj.* thin and weak; having little substance
Even though it was published, the dissertation put forth a very *tenuous* theory on animal intelligence.
syn: thin; unconvincing; fragile   *ant: strong; cogent*

15. **pithy** (pi´ thē) *adj.* full of meaning; concise
The *pithy* statements in greeting cards are often short and sweet.
syn: succinct   *ant: verbose*

Exercise I

Words in Context

From the list below, supply the words needed to complete the paragraph. Some words will not be used.

pristine	discordant	xenophobia	subjugate
impregnable	invective	pithy	inherent

1. Queen Alana's _____ was not entirely unfounded. During her twenty-year reign, her lands had been the victim of four separate invasions, two of which nearly _____ the tiny island to foreign rule. The enemies had already expressed views that were _____ with the Queen's about common borders. After issuing a fiery _____ questioning the foreign king's intentions, Queen Alana began to prepare for war. Two days later, the _____, old-world forest on the southern shore of her realm became crowded with invading troops, all of whom were preparing for an onslaught on the supposedly _____ castle.

From the list below, supply the words needed to complete the paragraph. Some words will not be used.

irreverent	filibuster	prodigal	torpid
inherent	expedite	pithy	tenuous

2. Despite four thousand years of erosion, the Egyptian hieroglyphics on the wall still carried a[n] _____ message: "Enter and be doomed." Murdoch, trying to _____ stealing the hidden treasure, paid no attention to the symbols as he raised his pickaxe over his head and sent it crashing into, but not through, the limestone wall. The native guide scolded Murdoch's _____ treatment of the ancient burial chamber, but Murdoch retorted with the quick explanation that etiquette was not a[n] _____ part of archaeological theft. Murdoch took a[n] _____ second swing, this time penetrating the wall. He grinned at the thought of what waited for him beyond the wall, unaware that the guide had become pale and stood in amazement next to the catacomb entrance, _____ and unable to escape.

From the list below, supply the words needed to complete the paragraph. Some words will not be used.

filibuster	torpid	subdued
xenophobia	prodigal	invective

3. Senator Melita Darnell knew that she would have to _____ to prevent a vote on the new McDermid Bill. To her, the bill would pave the way for the same _____ government spending that she had vowed to eliminate. Fortunately, the senator was able to identify others who held _____ opinions on the bill, and thus could be convinced to abstain from voting.

| Exercise II |

Sentence Completion

Complete the sentence in a way that shows you understand the meaning of the italicized vocabulary word.

1. The representative's *filibuster* prevented Congress from…

2. The *prodigal* lifestyle of the twin sisters caused the family to…

3. *Discordant* union members were blamed for lost work during the…

4. The surgeon called from Nebraska to tell the Maryland courier to *expedite* the…

5. The advertising department sought a *pithy* catchphrase for…

6. The car collector could tell by the *pristine* condition of the coupe that…

7. The mourners thought that Niles was *irreverent* to talk on his cell phone during…

8. Owing to unfounded *xenophobia*, some citizens fear…

9. The *impregnable* underground base proved to be impossible to…

10. The *subdued* animal had no idea…

11. Many of the laborers became *torpid* when the weather…

12. An *inherent* part of college life is…

13. The *tenuous* criticism of the show did not…

14. Ancient Rome *subjugated* its captured prisoners by…

15. Irene's loud *invective* to Jye caused everyone within earshot to…

Exercise III

Roots, Prefixes, and Suffixes

Study the entries and answer the questions that follow.

The roots *luc*, *lus*, and *lum* mean "light."
The prefix *il–* means "in."
The root *ten* means "to hold."
The roots *cur* and *cours* mean "to run" or "to go."

1. Using *literal* translations as guidance, define the following words without using a dictionary:

   A. illuminate   D. current
   B. curriculum   E. tenant
   C. tenet   F. luminosity

2. The root *lieu* means "place," so the literal translation of *lieutenant* is

   _____.

   If you deliver packages for people by running them from one place to another, your job title might be _____.

3. If *trans* means "through," then *translucent* means _____.
   If you prefer a particular brand of bread, then you probably have a[n]
   _____ to purchase that brand when you go shopping.

4. List all the words you can think of that contain the roots *lus*, *luc*, or *ten*.

5. List all the words you can think of that contain the roots *cur* or *cours*.

Exercise IV

Inference

Complete the sentences by inferring information about the italicized word from its context.

1. The security company told Iniko that his house was *impregnable*, so he was surprised when he got home and discovered that...

2. When you hear one driver shout *invectives* at another driver, you might assume that...

3. Someone going to a country in which the climate is *torpid* should...

Exercise V

Critical Reading

Below is a reading passage followed by several multiple-choice questions. Carefully read the passage and choose the best answer for each of the questions.

The following passage is adapted from Chapter 113, "The Forge," from Herman Melville's Moby-Dick *(1851).*

With matted beard, and swathed in a bristling shark-skin apron, about mid-day, Perth was standing between his forge and anvil, the latter placed upon an iron-wood log, with one hand holding a pike-head in the coals, and with the other at his forge's lungs, when Captain Ahab came along, carrying in his hand a small rusty-looking leathern bag. While yet a little distance from
5   the forge, moody Ahab paused; till at last, Perth, withdrawing his iron from the fire, began hammering it upon the anvil—the red mass sending off the sparks in thick hovering flights, some of which flew close to Ahab.

"Are these thy Mother Carey's chickens, Perth? they are always flying in thy wake; birds of good omen, too, but not to all;—look here, they burn; but thou— thou liv'st among them without
10   a scorch."

"Because I am scorched all over, Captain Ahab," answered Perth, resting for a moment on his hammer; "I am past scorching; not easily can'st thou scorch a scar."

"Well, well; no more. Thy shrunk voice sounds too calmly, sanely woeful to me. In no Paradise myself, I am impatient of all misery in others that is not mad. Thou should'st go mad,
15   blacksmith; say, why dost thou not go mad? How can'st thou endure without being mad? Do the heavens yet hate thee, that thou can'st not go mad?—What wert thou making there?"

"Welding an old pike-head, sir; there were seams and dents in it."

"And can'st thou make it all smooth again, blacksmith, after such hard usage as it had?"

"I think so, sir."
20   "And I suppose thou can'st smoothe almost any seams and dents; never mind how hard the metal, blacksmith?"

"Aye, sir, I think I can; all seams and dents but one."

"Look ye here, then," cried Ahab, passionately advancing, and leaning with both hands on Perth's shoulders; "look ye here—HERE—can ye smoothe out a seam like this, blacksmith,"
25   sweeping one hand across his ribbed brow; "if thou could'st, blacksmith, glad enough would I lay my head upon thy anvil, and feel thy heaviest hammer between my eyes. Answer! Can'st thou smoothe this seam?"

"Oh! that is the one, sir! Said I not all seams and dents but one?"

"Aye, blacksmith, it is the one; aye, man, it is unsmoothable; for though thou only see'st it
30   here in my flesh, it has worked down into the bone of my skull—THAT is all wrinkles! But, away with child's play; no more gaffs and pikes to-day. Look ye here!" jingling the leathern bag, as if it were full of gold coins. "I, too, want a harpoon made; one that a thousand yoke of fiends could not part, Perth; something that will stick in a whale like his own fin-bone. There's the stuff," flinging the pouch upon the anvil. "Look ye, blacksmith, these are the gathered nail-stubs of the steel
35   shoes of racing horses."

"Horse-shoe stubs, sir? Why, Captain Ahab, thou hast here, then, the best and stubbornest stuff we blacksmiths ever work."

"I know it, old man; these stubs will weld together like glue from the melted bones of

murderers. Quick! forge me the harpoon. And forge me first, twelve rods for its shank; then wind,
40   and twist, and hammer these twelve together like the yarns and strands of a tow-line. Quick! I'll
blow the fire."

When at last the twelve rods were made, Ahab tried them, one by one, by spiraling them,
with his own hand, round a long, heavy iron bolt. "A flaw!" rejecting the last one. "Work that over
again, Perth."

45   This done, Perth was about to begin welding the twelve into one, when Ahab stayed his
hand, and said he would weld his own iron. As, then, with regular, gasping hems, he hammered
on the anvil, Perth passing to him the glowing rods, one after the other, and the hard pressed
forge shooting up its intense straight flame, the Parsee passed silently, and bowing over his head
towards the fire, seemed invoking some curse or some blessing on the toil. But, as Ahab looked
50   up, he slid aside.

"What's that bunch of Lucifers dodging about there for?" muttered Stubb, looking on from
the forecastle. "That Parsee smells fire like a fusee; and smells of it himself, like a hot musket's
powder-pan."

At last the shank, in one complete rod, received its final heat; and as Perth, to temper it,
55   plunged it all hissing into the cask of water nearby, the scalding steam shot up into Ahab's bent
face.

"Would'st thou brand me, Perth?" wincing for a moment with the pain; "have I been but
forging my own branding-iron, then?"

"Pray God, not that; yet I fear something, Captain Ahab. Is not this harpoon for the White
60   Whale?"

"For the white fiend! But now for the barbs; thou must make them thyself, man. Here are
my razors—the best of steel; here, and make the barbs sharp as the needle-sleet of the Icy Sea."

For a moment, the old blacksmith eyed the razors as though he would fain not use them.

"Take them, man, I have no need for them; for I now neither shave, sup, nor pray till—but
65   here—to work!"

Fashioned at last into an arrowy shape, and welded by Perth to the shank, the steel soon
pointed the end of the iron; and as the blacksmith was about giving the barbs their final heat,
prior to tempering them, he cried to Ahab to place the water-cask near.

"No, no—no water for that; I want it of the true death-temper. Ahoy, there! Tashtego,
70   Queequeg, Daggoo! What say ye, pagans! Will ye give me as much blood as will cover this barb?"
holding it high up. A cluster of dark nods replied, Yes. Three punctures were made in the heathen
flesh, and the White Whale's barbs were then tempered.

"Ego non baptizo te in nomine patris, sed in nomine diaboli!" deliriously howled Ahab, as the
malignant iron scorchingly devoured the baptismal blood.

1A. "Perth" is
  A. the ship's blacksmith.
  B. the ship's cook.
  C. another name for the Parsee.
  D. a type of spear.
  E. the first mate.

1B. Which phrase from the passage best supports your answer to question 1A?
  A. "...Ahab came along, carrying in his hand a small rusty-looking leathern bag."
  B. "...the red mass sending off the sparks in thick hovering flights..."
  C. "...with one hand holding a pike-head in the coals..."
  D. "...Perth was standing between his forge and anvil..."
  E. "While yet a little distance from the forge, moody Ahab paused..."

2A. "Mother Carey's chickens" is a sailor's term for storm petrels, or small sea birds. The metaphor in lines 8-10 likens Perth to
  A. sea birds.
  B. a ship's wake.
  C. a ship in transit.
  D. a scar.
  E. a ship's captain.

2B. In the metaphor, the "chicken" refers to
  A. the sparks thrown from the anvil.
  B. the birds following Ahab's ship.
  C. the ghosts in Ahab's past.
  D. the pike Perth is working on.
  E. the omens Perth sees.

3A. Choose the answer that best paraphrases the following line (13-14):

  "In no Paradise myself, I am impatient of all misery in others that is not mad"?

  A. Because I am on my way to paradise, I do not deal with crazy people.
  B. Since I am marked for damnation, I have no time for people who think them selves crazy.
  C. As one who suffers, I have no patience for people who suffer from anything but madness.
  D. Join me in misery and allow yourself to go mad, where you can endure it.
  E. I am too mad to get into Paradise, so I spread my misery to others.

3B. According to lines 13-16, Ahab's solution to dealing with pain is to
  A. become numb, like the blacksmith.
  B. sail his ship.
  C. repair his psychological damage.
  D. make harpoons.
  E. allow himself to go crazy.

3C. Ahab's insistence that Perth repair his wounded head (lines 20-30) is a metaphor that suggests:
    A. Ahab will retire soon, because is he aged and wrinkled and wishes to end his suffering.
    B. Wise blacksmiths know that the human skull cannot withstand the heat of a forge.
    C. Ahab's wound is not merely physical; his mind is wounded, and he is irreparably insane.
    D. Perth serves a role as the ship's counselor, but knows that Ahab is beyond help.
    E. Ahab has been wounded by the white whale at some point in history.

4A. Which word best describes Perth's willingness to help Ahab?
    A. cautious
    B. calculating
    C. eager
    D. ecstatic
    E. devoted

4B. Choose the sentence from the text that best supports your answer to question 4A.
    A. "…thou hast here, then, the best and stubbornest stuff we blacksmiths ever work."
    B. "For the white fiend!"
    C. "Welding an old pike-head, sir; there were seams and dents in it."
    D. "Pray God, not that; yet I fear something, Captain Ahab."
    E. "Aye, sir, I think I can; all seams and dents but one."

5A. Ahab wishes for his harpoon not just to be deadly against whales, but also to
    A. be softer steel, so it is easy to sharpen.
    B. be stronger than monsters and murderers.
    C. have mysterious engravings on the blade.
    D. be a good weapon to use in fights.
    E. be used by Perth, its maker.

5B. Ahab provides two components for the manufacture of his harpoon. The shank is made of
    A. nails from race-horse shoes because it is the hardest steel available.
    B. melted mast screws because Ahab needs the razors for shaving.
    C. musket barrels and iron rods, for their tolerance to high heat.
    D. melted down gold coins, which he provides in a leather bag.
    E. the steel from the pike Perth had in the forge.

6. The actions of the Parsee make it seem as though he
    A. is watching the blacksmith to ensure that Ahab's harpoon is made properly.
    B. is comfortable or perhaps familiar with the unholy ceremony taking place.
    C. fears for his life amid a crew of heathens and an insane captain.
    D. knows the blacksmith personally because the Parsee bows to him.
    E. is looking for his religious artifacts but is frightened by something in the fire.

7A. Which statement best summarizes Ahab's declaration in lines 64-65?
    A. Ahab will forego everyday activities until the white whale is harpooned.
    B. Ahab intends to refrain from the normal behavior of a ship's captain.
    C. Everyday actions are not important to Ahab anymore.
    D. Donating the razors is Ahab's main contribution to the barb-making.
    E. Ahab is the only member of the crew who has the discipline to wield the harpoon.

7B. What substance does Ahab select for the tempering of the barbs on his newly forged harpoon?
   A.   sweat from the Parsee
   B.   saltwater from the sea
   C.   blood from the pagans
   D.   oil from the white whale
   E.   fire from the forge

8A. The imagery used in this scene is suggestive of
   A.   a witch's lair.
   B.   a factory floor.
   C.   a blacksmith's forge.
   D.   a biblical hell.
   E.   a typical whaling ship.

8B. Choose the elements of imagery from the text that *does not* support your answer to question 8A.
   A.   the flaming forge
   B.   the pouch
   C.   blood
   D.   the smell of gunpowder (sulfur)
   E.   howling

9A. At the end of the passage, Ahab howls a phrase in Latin that closes the scene in what most resembles
   A.   the undocking ceremony for a ship.
   B.   Ahab's last attempt to kill the whale.
   C.   an evil ritual marked by death and madness.
   D.   a party to help Perth's melancholy.
   E.   the Parsee's previous actions near the forge.

9B. Which detail[s] of the scene provides a clue that supports your answer to question 9A?
   A.   cluster of nods, iron
   B.   punctures, death-temper
   C.   White Whale's barbs
   D.   pagans
   E.   baptismal blood, heathen flesh

10. The best synonym for *malignant*, as it is used in line 74, is
   A.   evil.
   B.   sharp.
   C.   desperate.
   D.   rounded.
   E.   metal.

Review Lessons 16-18

Exercise I

Inferences

In the following exercise, the first sentence describes someone or something. Infer information from the first sentence, and then choose the word from the Word Bank that best completes the second sentence.

caustic	exodus	tenuous	taciturn
prodigal	irreverent	retribution	raconteur

1. Brandon has a story about everything, and when he tells one to a customer, he always get the sale.

    From this sentence, we can infer that Brandon is a good salesman because he is a[n] _____ .

2. Usually talkative, Leah has not spoken since her dog died over the weekend.

    From this sentence, we can infer that losing her pet has made Leah _____ .

3. The barbarians stormed into the city and defiled sacred landmarks, destroyed churches, and imprisoned priests, causing immediate outrage and hostile aggression from the resistance.

    From this sentence, we can infer that the invaders' _____ treatment of anything religious made their invasion more difficult.

4. The heir to the largest personal fortune in US history managed to waste the entire sum on luxuries and bad investments over the span of a single generation.

    From this sentence, we can infer that the _____ heir was irresponsible with money.

5. Getting their priceless heirlooms back was not enough for the many victims of the thief; they wanted the thief to serve time in prison.

    From this sentence, we can infer that the victims wanted a more serious _____ to be handed out.

Exercise II

Related Words

Some of the vocabulary words from Lessons 16 through 18 have related meanings. Complete the following sentences by choosing the word that best fits the context, based on information you infer from the use of the italicized word. Some word pairs will be antonyms, some will be synonyms, and some will simply be words often used in the same context.

1. The _____ professor of *linguistics* believed that speaking is not nearly as important as listening.
    A. taciturn
    B. rabid
    C. terse
    D. impregnable
    E. pithy

2. Genghis Khan's soldiers stormed through the city until they _____ all resistance, and then they *subjugated* the women and children, forcing them to carry the plunder back to the homeland, where they would then become slaves.
    A. piqued
    B. quelled
    C. scourged
    D. expedited
    E. reposed

3. The defensive *prowess* of the hockey team made their goal virtually _____ to all but the best opponents.
    A. agnostic
    B. pugnacious
    C. impregnable
    D. quixotic
    E. vindictive

4. Residents felt that the giant turbines of the proposed wind farm would be an *irreverent* blight upon the natural scenery of the _____ valley, which is a popular tourist destination for nature lovers in search of old forests.
    A. precocious
    B. rabid
    C. subdued
    D. pristine
    E. inherent

5.   The *prodigal* student received light punishments for his pranks at school, but
     when he tried to pull the same pranks as an adult at his job, he was labeled a[n]
     _____ and promptly fired.
     A.   renegade
     B.   retribution
     C.   exodus
     D.   uncanny
     E.   plebeian

6.   Police were forced to protect the notorious criminal from the _____ families of
     his victims, all of whom demanded *retribution* for his crimes.
     A.   predatory
     B.   caustic
     C.   penitent
     D.   vindictive
     E.   terse

7.   School officials agreed to *expedite* the extremely _____ third grader's education
     because she was clearly ready for high school academics.
     A.   rabid
     B.   taciturn
     C.   discordant
     D.   precocious
     E.   impregnable

8.   Franco's *quixotic* expectations of finding fame and fortune by discovering gold in the
     Yukon shadowed his _____ understanding of the sacrifices necessary for suc-
     cess in mining.
     A.   uncanny
     B.   inherent
     C.   tenuous
     D.   pristine
     E.   prodigal

9.   Angry incantations from the _____ easily drowned out the *pusillanimous*
     mayor's call for everyone to please calm down.
     A.   exodus
     B.   rabble
     C.   filibuster
     D.   xenophobia
     E.   raconteur

10. A textbook case of road rage led the two _____ drivers to engage in a fistfight
     after exchanging a series of vulgar *invectives* while stopped in heavy traffic.
     A.   uncanny
     B.   precocious
     C.   irreverent
     D.   subdued
     E.   pugnacious

Exercise III

Deeper Meanings

Choose a word to replace the italicized word in each sentence. All of the possible choices for each sentence have similar definitions, but the correct answer will have a connotation that best suits the context. For example, the words "delete," "destroy," and "obliterate" all mean "to remove or wipe out," but no one would ever say, "I destroyed the name from the document." The correct choice will be the word that has the best specific meaning and does not render the sentence awkward in tone or content. When choices seem close, look for a clue in the context that makes one choice better than the other.

Note that the correct answer is not always the primary vocabulary word from the lesson.

outdoor	cleared	angry	remorseful	rules
sorry	plebeian	vindicated	common	absolved
conquers	unforgiving	vindictive	subjugates	condemned

1. Medieval royalty frowned upon suntans for themselves because tans were characteristic of *lowly* activities, such as laboring in the fields.

   Better word: _____

2. The cowboys in the saloon never turned their backs on Earle after beating him at poker, because he was a[n] *mad* loser.

   Better word: _____

3. You'll be *penitent* if you wait until the night before the due date to write your research paper.

   Better word: _____

4. Confirmation of the discovery of the new element *fixed* the scientist's reputation, which had suffered because no one had believed him.

   Better word: _____

5. The gang lures runaway teenagers to its compound and then *represses* the victims, forcing them to engage in illegal, illicit activities for which the gang gets paid.

   Better word: _____

Exercise IV

Crossword Puzzle

Use the clues to complete the crossword puzzle. The answers consist of vocabulary words from Lessons 16 through 18.

Across

1. hold the audience hostage
3. looking to settle a score
6. barbarians at the gate
7. afraid of one's own shadow
9. another dish best served cold
10. not as painful as sticks or stones
11. wishing for a do-over
12. like a new-in-box action figure from 1984
13. ahead of the class
14. not sure of anything

Down

2. put to work
4. remove the blame
5. what a pickpocket does with your wallet
6. a little joshing
7. like a fox in a henhouse
8. like wearing a banana costume to a funeral
11. like the have-nots
13. to the point

Exercise V

Subject Prompts

Here is a writing prompt similar to the one you will find on the writing portion of an assessment test. Follow the instructions below and write a brief, efficient essay.

The subject of wages and salary might seem like a distant concern for students who have yet to commit to a job or career, but it is all too real for people in the working world, who must prove their own value on a daily basis by producing a product or providing a service. Unsurprisingly, there is as much disparity among wage earners as there is among personality types of everyone on Earth.

Consider one career choice that is known to pay a large salary and one career in which the wages are far too low. Argue whether the careers you select should or should not command high wages, comparing them in the process.

Support your arguments with facts, details, and examples, and remember to address counterarguments to your position while you construct your essay.

Thesis: Write a *one-sentence* response to the above assignment. Make certain this single sentence offers a clear statement of your position.

Example: It is embarrassing that the people who are required to be in harm's way on a daily basis earn a fraction of those people who simply entertain bored people.

_____

_____

Organizational Plan: List at least three subtopics you will use to support your main idea. This list is your outline.

1. _____

2. _____

3. _____

Draft: Following your outline, write a good first draft of your essay. Remember to support all your points with examples, facts, references to reading, etc.

Review and Revise: Exchange essays with a classmate. Using the scoring guide for Organization on page 257, score your partner's essay (while he or she scores yours). Focus on the organizational plan and the use of language conventions. If necessary, rewrite your essay to improve the organizational plan and/or your use of language.

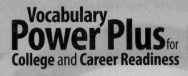

Lesson Nineteen

1. **vacuous** (va´ kyə wəs) *adj.* lacking intelligence; empty of reason
The student's *vacuous* expression revealed his failure to study for the test.
syn: empty-headed   *ant: brilliant; shrewd*

2. **epicurean** (e pi kyū´ rē ən) *adj.* taking pleasure in food and drink
The *epicurean* chef taught his students not only how to cook food, but also how to enjoy it.
syn: hedonistic; gourmet

3. **coup** (kōō) *n.* a surprising, brilliant, and usually successful act
The rebels planned a *coup* to overthrow the current Prime Minister and install a new leader.
syn: plot

4. **oeuvre** (ə´ vrə) *n.* the complete work of an artist, composer, or writer
Shakespeare's *oeuvre* is one of the most respected groups of literary works ever written.
syn: canon

5. **verdant** (vər´ dənt) *adj.* fresh and green, referring to plant life
The *verdant* landscape reminded the O'Connells of their native Ireland so much that they decided to build a home there.
syn: lush   *ant: arid; sere*

6. **commensurate** (kə men´ sər it) *adj.* an equal measure; corresponding in size and measurement
Though Margie and Liz attended different universities, they received *commensurate* educations.
syn: equivalent; comparable   *ant: unequal*

7. **attrition** (ə tri´ shən) *n.* a wearing down over time
The company faced a severe *attrition* of its stock price because of bad publicity.
syn: erosion   *ant: buildup; accretion*

8. **vagary** (vā´ gə rē) *n.* unpredictable action or behavior
Kristin's *vagaries* prevented her from holding a job as an air traffic controller.
syn: whim; caprice

9. **approbation** (a prə bā´ shən) *n.* formal approval of an act
The president gave his *approbation* for the rescue of ten citizens who were being held hostage at a foreign embassy.
syn: authorization   *ant: disapproval; opprobrium*

10. **burgeon** (bər´ jən) *v.* to grow, expand, or bloom
Increased colonization caused the island city to *burgeon*.
syn: swell   *ant: shrink; diminish*

11. **mellifluous** (mə li´ flōō wəs) *adj.* having a rich, smoothly flowing sound
The singer's *mellifluous* voice contributed to the relaxed atmosphere of the lounge.
syn: harmonious   *ant: strident; discordant*

12. **archetype** (är´ ki tīp) *n.* a prototype or original model
The *archetype* for the first airplane was only a toy model, but it has led to modern jets
and supersonic fighter planes.
syn: model   *ant: product*

13. **secular** (se´ kyə lər) *adj.* not spiritual or religious; worldly
Many religions warn of the dangers of the *secular* world because they believe it is full
of sin.
syn: earthly   *ant: religious*

14. **confluence** (kän´ flōō əns) *n.* a meeting or gathering together
The United Nations General Assembly is a *confluence* of world thought.
syn: convergence; concourse   *ant: divergence*

15. **arbiter** (är´ bə tər) *n.* a person with the ability to resolve a disagreement; a judge
The principal ended the conflict by acting as an *arbiter* between the two angry
students.

Exercise I

Words in Context

From the list below, supply the words needed to complete the paragraph. Some words will not be used.

arbiter	vacuous	burgeon	commensurate
vagary	secular		

1. As the terrorist threat _____ each year in the United States, citizens must raise their vigilance to _____ levels. Citizens must also hinder terrorist intelligence-gathering capabilities by implementing small irregularities in their day-to-day routines. These intentional _____ in behavior will prevent terrorists from determining the best time to attack. We must learn to vary concentrations of people, control the distribution of work schedules, and otherwise keep terrorists as _____ as possible about our daily routines.

From the list below, supply the words needed to complete the paragraph. Some words will not be used.

archetype	verdant	attrition	confluence
epicurean	mellifluous	coup	

2. Tonia closed her eyes to concentrate better on the _____ sounds of the mambo orchestra playing at Anconia's Night Club. She heard only what emanated through the rear wall. She would stand next to the wall, close her eyes, and imagine that she was a member of the _____ clientele feasting at the glass tables in Anconia's impressive ballroom. Just a week earlier, Tonia had met Anconia's doorman after the club had closed for the night, and he was nice enough to allow her inside for a look. The walls around the dance floor and dining area were _____ with dangling, subtropical plants, and the dance floor sparkled even though the club was fifty years old. Impressed, Tonia realized how Anconia's provided a place for the _____ of the wealthy and the famous.

From the list below, supply the words needed to complete the paragraph. Some words will not be used.

oeuvre	arbiter	attrition	archetype
approbation	coup	secular	vagary

3. J.T. Fleming, donning a beret and sitting in a raised, wooden folding chair, seemed to be a perfect _____ of the Hollywood director. With two science fiction blockbusters in his _____ that had made over $1 billion worldwide, Fleming had come to enjoy the _____ of all his investors, until his latest production.

    In a departure from _____ films, Fleming now wanted to make a masterpiece based on religious themes. Afraid that the film might offend many patrons, the investors began to plot a[n] _____ against Fleming and slowly pulled their funding for the project. The consequent lawsuits over the contracts between the studio and the investors kept _____ working for months determining who owed money, and the lengthy delay in production caused a[n] _____ of interest in the film, eventually leading it to open poorly at the box office.

Exercise II

Sentence Completion

Complete the sentence in a way that shows you understand the meaning of the italicized vocabulary word.

1. To prove that he was not as *vacuous* as everyone thought, Gene...

2. The *confluence* of the rivers enabled...

3. The *epicurean* restaurant owner paled when her doctor told her that...

4. The *vagaries* and unpredictability of the hurricane...

5. Roslyn found it easy to drift off to the *mellifluous* sounds of...

6. Before taking the case to court, the companies brought in an *arbiter* to...

7. Tycho's *verdant* front yard resembled...

8. The increase in student *attrition* in the advanced class caused...

9. Unlike the traditional *archetype* of the mad scientist, Hans looks and behaves more like...

10. The vice-president of the corporation gave his *approbation* to finance the...

11. If the deadly bacteria in the dish *burgeon* uncontrollably, the scientist will...

12. Had the *coup* against Lincoln succeeded completely, the country now known as the United States would...

13. Picasso's *oeuvre* was the topic of conversation during...

14. Bonnie and Doug opted for a *secular* wedding because...

15. Though Kaneka and Robin grew up in different places, they had *commensurate* levels of...

Exercise III

Roots, Prefixes, and Suffixes

Study the entries and answer the questions that follow.

The root *cogn* means "to know."
The root *ped* means "foot."
The root *ject* means "to throw."
The prefix *inter–* means "between."
The prefix *in–* means "not."
The prefix *de–* means "down."
The prefix *im–* means "on, against."

1. Using *literal* translations as guidance, define the following words without using a dictionary:

    A. interject   D. impediment
    B. incognito   E. pedestrian
    C. dejected   F. cognitive

2. If you need foot surgery, you will probably go to a[n]_____.

    An insect that seems to have a thousand legs is called a[n] _____.

3. Bullets, arrows, and rocks that are thrown from catapults are types of _____.

    If *pro–* means "before," then a *prognosis* is knowledge about _____.

4. List all the words that you can think of that contain the roots *cogn*, *ped*, and *ject*.

Exercise IV

Inference

Complete the sentences by inferring information about the italicized word from its context.

1. One explanation for the *confluence* of pigeons and robins on the street is…

2. If you paint your house a *verdant* green, your neighbors might tell you…

3. A good reason for peasants to organize a *coup* against their ruler is…

Exercise V

Writing

Here is a writing prompt similar to the one you will find on the writing portion of an assessment test.

Plan and write an essay based on the following statement:

> In August of 1862, Horace Greeley, editor of the *New York Tribune*, wrote an editorial in which he criticized President Abraham Lincoln's administration as "lacking direction and resolve," and in which he demanded the emancipation of American slaves. A few days later, Abraham Lincoln sent a reply in which he said, "My paramount object in this struggle is to save the Union....If I could save the Union without freeing any slave, I would do it; and if I could save it by freeing all the slaves, I would do it; and if I could save it by freeing some and leaving others alone, I would also do that."

Assignment: Write an essay in which you explain Lincoln's response to Horace Greeley. Use evidence from your reading, your studies, your observations, and your experience to support and develop your points of explanation. Ask yourself if the statement changes the way you understand the historical context.

Thesis: Write a *one-sentence* response to the above assignment. Make certain this single sentence offers a clear statement of your position.

Example: The Civil War might have brought the end of slavery, but according to president Abraham Lincoln, the nation's first mission was to preserve the Union.

_____

_____

Organizational Plan: List at least three subtopics you will use to support your main idea. This list is your outline.

1. _____

2. _____

3. _____

Draft: Following your outline, write a good first draft of your essay. Remember to support all your points with examples, facts, references to reading, etc.

Review and Revise: Exchange essays with a classmate. Using the Holistic scoring guide on page 262, score your partner's essay (while he or she scores yours). If necessary, rewrite your essay to correct the problems noted by your partner.

Exercise VI

Improving Paragraphs

Read the following passage and then answer the multiple-choice questions that follow. The questions will require you to make decisions regarding the revision of the reading selection.

1   (1) In 1891, Jay Gould, a wealthy railroad magnate, promised to rebuild a church in Roxbury, New York. (2) As a member of the church he had vowed to build, Gould knew that the previous building had been prone to storms and fires, he pledged to fund stone construction of the church, which is what had recently destroyed the church. (3) Never getting to see the church that was built with his money by his children, he died in 1892, but the church that Gould promised definitely was built.

2   (4) The church just happened to be erected right next to a house that had been built 30 years earlier, and one that Gould's daughter, Helen, fancied. (5) Not long after the church was completed, Helen bought the estate and named it "Kirkside" for its position adjacent to the neighboring Kirkside Lake. (6) The house was built by Liberty Preston.

3   (7) After Gould's death, his six children took up the cause and even financed the project. (8) Construction began in 1893 for the early English Gothic-style church built with rough-faced St. Lawrence marble. (9) In 1894, the dedication of the building honored Jay Gould, and the structure was named for him.

4   (10) When Helen died in 1938, the beauty of Kirkside became available to many other people. (11) Twelve acres of the estate have since become Kirkside Park, a center of activity in Roxbury. (12) Helen's brother donated the house to the Reformed Church of America as a retirement home for clerics and their families. (13) Eventually, the home was opened to elderly persons of all denominations.

1. To improve paragraph 1, sentence 2 should be
    A. deleted.
    B. broken into two sentences.
    C. moved to follow sentence 3.
    D. combined with sentences 1 and 2.
    E. left unchanged.

2. Choose the best revision of sentence 3.
    A. Gould died in 1892, long before the project was finished, but his children ensured that his promise went fulfilled.
    B. Before dying in 1892, Gould did not get to see the church built, though his children did, using their inheritance.
    C. The church was not built before Gould died in 1892, but his children used his money for the same purpose.
    D. Before his promise was fulfilled, Gould died, and, in 1892, his children rebuilt the church.
    E. When Gould died in 1892, the church could not be rebuilt unless Gould's children continued the project, which they did happily, though Gould did not get to see the final product.

3. Which of the following suggestions would improve the organization of the passage?
   A. Exchange paragraph 4 with paragraph 2.
   B. Exchange paragraph 3 with paragraph 1.
   C. Exchange paragraph 4 with paragraph 3.
   D. Exchange paragraph 1 with paragraph 4.
   E. Exchange paragraph 3 with paragraph 2.

4. Which sentence could be deleted without changing the intent of the passage?
   A. sentence 4
   B. sentence 5
   C. sentence 6
   D. sentence 7
   E. sentence 8

5. Choose the most appropriate title for the passage.
   A. Two Parks for the Price of One
   B. Legacy of a Robber Baron
   C. Jay Gould's Kirkside Home
   D. The Gift of Gould
   E. Children of Wealth

Lesson Twenty

1. **demur** (di mər´) *v.* to disapprove or to take exception
   Martin *demurred* when Sandy suggested that they spend Friday evening at the ballet.
   syn: object; disagree   *ant: agree; acquiesce*

2. **fixed** (fiksd) *adj.* stuck in place or position
   Kelsey prefers a bicycle with *fixed* gears because it has fewer parts to repair.
   syn: immovable; rigid; stationary   *ant: changeable; variable*

3. **dissident** (di´ sə dənt) *n.* someone who disagrees
   The *dissidents* of the proposed welfare bill staged a protest.
   syn: renegade   *ant: supporter*

4. **stipulate** (sti´ pyə lāt) *v.* to specify a required part of an agreement
   The developer *stipulated* that before construction could begin, the homeowners must
   first provide a down payment.
   syn: require

5. **tenet** (te´ nət) *n.* a belief or principle held to be true
   Belief in the Holy Trinity is one of the main *tenets* of Catholicism.
   syn: cornerstone; creed

6. **ruminate** (rōō´ mə nāt) *v.* to think deeply or repeatedly
   The great philosopher could often be found *ruminating* over the question of death.
   syn: ponder; reflect

7. **vigilant** (vi´ jə lent) *adj.* alert at all times; watchful
   The family's watchdog remained *vigilant* during the day, but he fell into a deep sleep
   at night.
   syn: alert   *ant: oblivious*

8. **proliferate** (prə li´ fə rāt) *v.* to grow or reproduce rapidly
   The plant food enabled Bob's irises to *proliferate* throughout the flower bed.
   syn: multiply   *ant: diminish*

9. **accolade** (a´ kə lād) *n.* an award or honor
   The reporter received *accolades* for her newest article that uncovered a serious
   money-laundering scandal.
   syn: kudos; recognition   *ant: opprobrium*

10. **belligerent** (bə li´ jə rənt) *adj.* ready to fight or argue
    Mike's *belligerent* remarks toward his boss cost him his job.
    syn: hostile; combative   *ant: friendly; agreeable*

11. **invidious** (in vi´ dē əs)   *adj.*   tending to cause discontent, harm, or resentment; offensively unfair
The *invidious* book caused a huge controversy over implications that a leading presidential candidate committed a crime.
syn: malicious   *ant: conciliatory*

12. **derivative** (də ri´ və tiv)   *n.*   not the original; coming from another source
The modern English word "engine" is a *derivative* of the Latin word "ingenium."
syn: offspring; branch

13. **zeitgeist** (zīt´ gīst)   *n.*   the general spirit of the time
Some consider the *zeitgeist* of the 1960s to be one of moral decay, while others see it as a time of reform.

14. **insouciant** (in sōō´ sē ənt)   *adj.*   not concerned; free from care
Jenna's *insouciant* attitude made her easy to befriend.
syn: nonchalant   *ant: worried*

15. **limpid** (lim´ pəd)   *adj.*   transparent; clear
The warm, *limpid* waters of the Aegean Sea provide excellent snorkeling opportunities.
                                                              ant: murky

Exercise I

Words in Context

From the list below, supply the words needed to complete the paragraph. Some words will not be used.

limpid	proliferate	tenet	ruminate	accolade
zeitgeist	stipulate	insouciant	fixed	dissident

1. Thirty years of saving money finally paid off when Vernita found the cottage of her dreams on the coast of Maine—or so she thought. Despite a handful of local _____, the Clifftown Historical Society approved the sale of the property, but not before they _____ one important factor: the new owner must keep the windmill in operating condition because it had been a landmark of the town for generations. Shrugging off the windmill as a minor concern, Vernita seized the opportunity to purchase the lot. Six months later, Vernita learned why the _____ of the cottage's original era included a rigorous work ethic.

    The problems began when she walked outside on a breezy morning and noticed the _____ blades of the windmill, despite the considerable breeze. The shaft to the millstones had broken, and its repair required nearly two thousand dollars and three weeks of toiling for her and two paid workmen. Two days after completing the repairs, the well began to pump a muddy, undrinkable liquid instead of its usual cool, _____ spring water. While contractors dug a new well, Vernita discovered that mold and insects had _____ in the dank basement. The unending problems caused Vernita to _____ on why she had ever bought the house. She had always believed in one _____: Sometimes, people just have to know when to quit. Vernita also missed the _____ life that she had while renting someone else's property. Three months later, Vernita moved back into a condominium.

From the list below, supply the words needed to complete the paragraph. Some words will not be used.

fixed	accolade	vigilant	belligerent
invidious	derivative	stipulate	

2. "Keep your _____ comments to yourself," said Kyle. "We have enough to worry about without fighting among ourselves. We needed a pilot, and Brad was the only team member who even came close."

    Lee Ann stopped complaining, but she thought again of how she foolishly _____ to Logan's half-witted escape plan, which she felt could cause _____ harm or even death. They were to grab the canisters, sneak out of the compound, run through the jungle, and steal one of the two old cargo planes on the dirt runway. Two team members had already been wounded, and Brad wasn't about to win any _____ for his abilities to get the dilapidated machine off the ground.

    "This plane's no good!" screamed Brad. "The left engine must need maintenance!"

"Let's try the other plane before the alarm sounds!" yelled Lee Ann. The team grabbed what little gear they had left, exited the plane, and hurried across the tarmac. Knowing that Benedito's security force would soon descend on them, the Americans remained _____ even as they scrambled to the other plane with their gear. While boarding, Kyle flinched when he looked beyond the flaps and caught sight of motorcycles entering the runway from the access road to the compound.

"Fire it up! Now!" yelled Kyle as he crawled over the team and landed with a thud in the primitive cockpit. "And check the canisters!"

Lee Ann checked. Luckily, the two quart-sized stainless steel canisters were intact and sealed; after all, one milligram of Prenitite would be more than enough to stop the hearts of everyone on the plane. A[n] _____ of the Prentonica seed, Prenitite was the number one item on every terrorist's wishlist.

Exercise II

Sentence Completion

Complete the sentence in a way that shows you understand the meaning of the italicized vocabulary word.

1. I would have bought the car, but the dealer *stipulated* that…

2. Chloe received *accolades* for exposing the corporate cover-up, but then her boss…

3. Displeased with the mayor's decision, several *dissidents*…

4. The tide pools are so *limpid* that you can see…

5. Your *belligerent* attitude toward customers has…

6. The reformists decided that the present *zeitgeist* did not…

7. The *vigilant* soldier on night watch heard the…

8. The Church declared that the work of art was too *invidious*, so it was displayed for one day before…

9. My moral *tenets* prevent me from helping you to…

10. If you *ruminate* too much before you swing the bat, you'll definitely…

11. As landmines *proliferate*, special United Nations teams…

12. The mayor realized his mistake when the *insouciant* toll bridge operator…

13. I *demurred* when asked to…

14. From the Greek root "chron," we get the *derivative* word…

15. The *fixed* pendulum meant that the clock was…

Exercise III

Roots, Prefixes, and Suffixes

Study the entries and answer the questions that follow.

The roots *cord* and *card* mean "heart" or "mind."
The roots *quis* and *quir* mean "to seek."
The prefix *ac–* means "towards."
The prefix *in–* means "into."
The prefix *cata–* means "down" or "thoroughly."
The root *tonia* means "paralysis."
The root *clysm* means "flood, disaster."

1. Using *literal* translations as guidance, define the following words without using a dictionary:

    A. inquisitive   D. catatonia
    B. discordant   E. cataclysm
    C. acquisitive   F. cordial

2. An agreement among nations to stop a particular behavior is sometimes called a[n]

    _____.

    Explain why the word *catapult* would use the "to put down" form of *cata–*. Repeat the process for the word *catalog*.

3. The purpose of an *inquisition* is to _____.
    If the prefix *re–* means "again," what is the literal translation of *record* (verb form)?

4. List as many words as you can that contain the roots *cord*, *quis*, or the prefix *cata–*.

Exercise IV

Inference

Complete the sentences by inferring information about the italicized word from its context.

1. If the political *dissident* does not publicly retract his statement, the dictator might…

2. Rumors of executives stealing from the company continue to *proliferate* because…

3. If the pond is no longer *limpid* after the factory begins production, you might assume that…

Exercise V

Critical Reading

Below is a pair of reading passages followed by several multiple-choice questions. Carefully read the passages and choose the best answer for each of the questions.

From 1804 to 1806, Meriwether Lewis and William Clark led the first official overland expedition to the Pacific Coast. At the time the following passages were written, the expedition party was near the Columbia River, which forms the current border between Washington and Oregon.

Passage 1
Sunday, April 20, 1806 (Captain Lewis):

Some frost this morning. The Eneeshur and Skilloots are much better clad than they were last fall; their men have generally leggings, moccasins, and large robes; many of them wear shirts of the same form with those of the Shoshone Chopunnish, highly ornamented with porcupine quills. The dress of their women differs very little from those of the great rapids and above. Their
5   children frequently wear robes of the large grey squirrel skins, those of the men and women are principally deer skins, some wolf, elk, bighorn, and buffalo; the latter they procure from the nations who sometimes visit the Missouri. Indeed a considerable proportion of their wearing apparel is purchased from their neighbors to the northwest in exchange for pounded fish, copper, and beads. At present, the principal village of the Eneeshur is below the falls on the north side of
10   the river. One other village is above the falls on the south side and another a few miles above on the north side. The first consists of nineteen, the second of eleven, and the third of five lodges. Their houses, like those of the Skilloots, have their floors on the surface of the ground, but are formed of sticks and covered with mats and straw. They are large and contain usually several families each. For fuel, they use straw, small willows, and the southern wood. They use the silk grass
15   in manufacturing their fishing nets and bags, and the bear grass and cedar bark are employed in forming a variety of articles. They are poor, dirty, proud, haughty, inhospitable, parsimonious, and faithless in every respect; nothing but our numbers, I believe, prevents their attempting to murder us at this moment.

This morning I was informed that the natives had pilfered six tomahawks and a knife from
20   the party in the course of the last night. I spoke to the chief on this subject. He appeared angry with his people and addressed them, but the property was not restored. One horse which I had purchased and paid for yesterday, and which could not be found when I ordered the horses into close confinement yesterday, I was now informed had been gambled away by the rascal who had sold it to me and had been taken away by a man of another nation. I therefore took the goods
25   back from this fellow. I purchased a gun from the chief for which I gave him two elk skins. In the course of the day, I obtained two other indifferent horses for which I gave an extravagant price. I found that I should get no more horses and therefore resolved to proceed tomorrow morning with those which I had and to convey the baggage in two small canoes that the horses could not carry. For this purpose, I had a load made up for seven horses; the eighth Bratton was compelled to ride
30   as he was yet unable to walk. I bartered my elk skins, old irons, and two canoes for beads. One of the canoes for which they would give us but little, I had cut up for fuel. These people have yet a large quantity of dried fish on hand, yet they will not let us have any but for an exorbitant price.

We purchased two dogs and some shappellel from them. I had the horses grazed until evening and then picketed and hobbled them within the limits of our camp. I ordered the indians from our
35   camp this evening and informed them that if I caught them attempting to purloin any article from us, I would beat them severely. They went off in rather a bad humor, and I directed the party to examine their arms and be **vigilant**. They stole two spoons from us in the course of the day. The Scaddals, Squan-nan-os, Shan-wah-purrs, and Shallattas reside to the northwest of these people, and depend on hunting deer and elk and trade with these people for their pounded fish.

Passage 2
Sunday, April 20, 1806 (Captain Clark):

This morning very cold; hills covered with snow. I showed the natives what I had to give for their horses and attempted to purchase them. They informed me that they would not sell any horses to me, that their horses were at a long ways off and they would not trade them. My offer was a blue robe, a calico shirt, a handkerchief, five parcels of paint, a knife, a wampum moon,
5   four braces of ribbon, a piece of brass, and about six braces of yellow beads; and to that amount for what I had, I also offered my large blue blanket for one, my coat, sword and plume—none of which seemed to entice those people to give horses if they had any. They sat in their huts, which are mats supported on poles without fire. At night, when they wish a light, they burn dry straw and some small, dry willows. They speak different from those below, and have but little to eat.
10   Some roots and dried fish are to be found in their houses. I am half frozen at this inhospitable village, which is moved from its position above the falls to one below, and contains nineteen large houses. A village is also established on the other side, immediately above the falls. All the natives who were established above the falls for some distance have moved. Those people are much better dressed than they were at the time we went down the river. They have all new deer, elk, ibex,
15   goat, and wolf skin robes, their children have also the large squirrel skin robes. Many of them have leggings and moccasins, all of which they procure from the indians at a distance in exchange for their pounded fish and beads. They also purchase silk grass, of which they make their nets and sails for taking fish. They also purchase bear grass and many other things for their fish. Those people gave me roots and berries prepared in different ways, for which I gave some small articles
20   in return. Great numbers of skimming nets on their houses. Those people are poor and kind of dirty and indolent. They wear their hair loose and flowing; the men cut in the forward, which the Skilloots do not.

I could not procure a single horse from those people, during this day, at any price. They offered me two for two kettles, of which we could not spare. I used every artifice decent and even
25   false statements to induce those poor devils to sell me horses. In the evening, two different men offered to sell me three horses, which they informed me were a little distance off and they would bring them immediately. Those two persons, as I found, went immediately off up the river to their tribe without any intention to find or sell their horses. A little before sunset, three men arrived from some distance above and informed me that they came to see me. At sunset, finding no prob-
30   ability of Captain Lewis' arrival, I packed up the articles and took them into the lodge in which I lay last night. Great numbers of those people gathered around me to smoke. I gave them two pipes and lay down in the back part of the house with Sgt. P. and the men with our arms situated as to be ready in case of any alarm. Those poor people appear entirely harmless—I purchased a dog and some wood with a little pounded fish and shappellels. Made a fire on the rocks and
35   cooked the dogs on which the men breakfasted and dined. Wind was hard all day, cold and from the northwest.

1A. Lewis's party (passage 1) lacks enough horses to carry all the equipment, so Lewis
   A.   hires Skilloots to help him carry the gear.
   B.   burns anything that he cannot carry.
   C.   purchases eight more horses.
   D.   transports the equipment in canoes.
   E.   purchases dogs to pull a sled.

1B. According to passage 1, one horse does not carry equipment because
   A.   the horse is unable to walk.
   B.   it is Captain Bratton's expensive show horse.
   C.   the equipment is placed in canoes.
   D.   the horse is stubborn and refuses to cross the river.
   E.   it must carry Bratton, an injured member of the party.

2A. As used in line 34 of passage 1, *hobbled* most nearly means
   A.   bartered away.
   B.   removed the horseshoes.
   C.   loaded down.
   D.   tied the legs to restrict movement.
   E.   staggered, as from leg wounds.

2B. What is the probable secondary motive suggested in passage 1 for Lewis's having *hobbled* the horses?
   A.   to prepare them to be eaten by the starving expedition party
   B.   to make the horses more difficult to steal
   C.   to prepare the horses to sell to the Native Americans
   D.   to ensure the horses did not use up their energy
   E.   to keep the horses calm

3.   Lewis describes the Native Americans as *parsimonious*, which means "cheap" or "stingy," in the same context in which he describes them as "poor." What personal reason might Lewis have for using what would seem to be a redundant description of the perceived frugality of the Eneeshur?
   A.   the Eneeshur's rudimentary construction practices
   B.   Lewis's superior attention to detail in recording his observations
   C.   the Eneeshur's bartering food for clothing with other nations
   D.   the Eneeshur's price for the equipment Lewis needs
   E.   Lewis's shock that the Eneeshur use willow and stray as fuel

4A. Which information can be inferred from passage 2, paragraph 2?
   A.   Lewis and Clark are lost somewhere near the Pacific coast.
   B.   The natives treat Clark better than they treat Lewis.
   C.   Lewis and Clark were not together in the same camp.
   D.   Clark successfully convinces the natives to sell horses.
   E.   Lewis is waiting for Clark to arrive.

4B. Choose the phrase that best supports your answer to question 4A.
   A.   "I...lay down...with our arms situated as to be ready in case of any alarm."
   B.   "They offered me two for two kettles, of which we could not spare."
   C.   "they informed me were a little distance off and they would bring them immediately"
   D.   "At sunset, finding no probability of Captain Lewis' arrival, I packed up the articles"
   E.   "Made a fire on the rocks and cooked the dogs on which the men breakfasted"

5A. As used in line 24 of passage 2, *artifice* most nearly means
   A.   an obvious lie.
   B.   a crafty maneuver.
   C.   currency.
   D.   a threatening statement.
   E.   a false promise.

5B. In addition to the *artifice*, what other method does Clark use to try to purchase horses?
   A.   trading medicine
   B.   offering kettles
   C.   teaching
   D.   lying
   E.   threats

6A. What can be inferred from Clark's description of the Eneeshur and Skilloot's clothing?
   A.   They do not craft all of their own clothing.
   B.   Too much curing ruins the leather of the moccasins.
   C.   The Native Americans do not like to travel while wearing skins.
   D.   The clothing is superior protection from rain.
   E.   The quality of clothing reflects a warrior's success.

6B. To purchase clothing, the Eneeshur and Skilloot Indians used
   A.   kettles.
   B.   buffalo hides.
   C.   shappellel.
   D.   pounded fish.
   E.   calico.

7A. Which statement is *false* at the time the journal entries were written?
   A.   Lewis and Clark had not previously met the Eneeshur and Skilloot.
   B.   One Eneeshur village contained nineteen lodges.
   C.   The expedition teams needed horses.
   D.   The expedition teams ate dogs.
   E.   Porcupine quills were a valuable source of nutrition.

7B. Choose the phrase from passage 1 that best supports your answer to question 7A.
   A.   "The first consists of nineteen, the second of eleven, and the third of five lodges."
   B.   "I obtained two other indifferent horses for which I gave an extravagant price."
   C.   "The Eneeshur and Skilloots are much better clad than they were last fall"
   D.   "One horse which I had purchased...had been gambled away by the rascal who had sold it to me"
   E.   "They are...faithless in every respect"

8A. Lewis and Clark do not agree
   A. on the weather conditions.
   B. on the general physical appearance of the natives.
   C. that there is a need for more horses.
   D. on the level of threat posed by the natives.
   E. that the Eneeshur and Skilloots are fishermen.

8B. Choose the phrase from passage 1 that best supports your answer to question 8A.
   A. "nothing but our numbers, I believe, prevents their attempting to murder us at this moment"
   B. "the natives had pilfered six tomahawks and a knife"
   C. "The dress of their women differs very little from those of the great rapids"
   D. "They are poor, dirty, proud, haughty, inhospitable"
   E. "I purchased a gun from the chief for which I gave him two elk skins"

8C. Choose the phrase from passage 2 that best supports your answer to question 8A.
   A. "Those people gave me roots and berries prepared in different ways, for which I gave some small articles in return"
   B. "Great numbers of those people gathered around me to smoke"
   C. "I could not procure a single horse from those people"
   D. "They speak different from those below, and have but little to eat"
   E. "Those poor people appear entirely harmless"

9A. Which choice best describes the difference in tone between the passages?
   A. Passage 2 is more detached and impersonal than passage 1.
   B. Passage 1 betrays Lewis's anxiety; passage 2 contains few negative terms.
   C. Clark (passage 2) does not refer to himself in the first person.
   D. Clark (passage 2) is upset about the thefts, and Lewis (passage 1) is not.
   E. Passage 1 is spirited and lively, while passage 2 is serious and solemn.

9B. Which element of passage 1 best supports your answer to question 9A?
   A. the expedition's shortage of horses
   B. Lewis's unfamiliarity with the Native Americans at the camp
   C. the theft of tools from the expedition party
   D. Lewis's descriptions of his hosts and his misgivings about them
   E. the captain's act of cutting up a canoe for fuel

10. In their journal entries, neither Lewis nor Clark mentions
   A. the location of the Shallatta Indians.
   B. the weather conditions.
   C. the locations of the Eneeshur villages.
   D. the characteristics of the native dwellings.
   E. the distance the party plans to travel the next day.

Lesson Twenty-One

1. **asinine** (as´ ə nīn) *adj.* exhibiting poor judgment or intelligence
   Jonah revealed his *asinine* tendencies when he rudely insulted the rabbi.
   syn: foolish; boorish; silly   *ant: sagacious*

2. **indefatigable** (in di fat´ i gə bəl) *adj.* tireless; incapable of being fatigued
   Dave was so passionate about his work that he seemed almost *indefatigable* to the rest of the group.
           ant: exhausted

3. **ancillary** (an´ si lə rē) *adj.* subsidiary; providing assistance
   The senior executive of the firm hired an *ancillary* worker to do his filing and typing.

4. **osmosis** (äz mō´ səs) *n.* a gradual, often unconscious, process of absorption
   Living in a foreign country allowed Jerry to learn its language by *osmosis*.

5. **autodidact** (ô tō dī´ dakt) *n.* a self-taught person
   With accomplishments in law, politics, and literature, Abe Lincoln is perhaps the most famous *autodidact* in American history.
   syn: self-educated

6. **albeit** (ôl bē´ ət) *conj.* although; even though
   It was rainy and miserable all summer, *albeit* good for the crops.

7. **behest** (bi hest´) *n.* a command or urgent request
   Tyler grudgingly obeyed his mother's *behest* to come home early after the school dance.
   syn: demand

8. **philatelist** (fə lat´ əl ist) *n.* one who collects stamps
   As a prominent *philatelist*, Dr. James has over ten thousand stamps in his collection.

9. **indiscretion** (in dis kresh´ ən) *n.* a minor misdeed
   If it is scandalous enough, a single *indiscretion* can cost a politician his or her career.
   syn: peccadillo; transgression

10. **picayune** (pi kē yōōn´) *adj.* of very little value; trivial; inconsequential
    Mike's *picayune* collection of toy trucks had more sentimental value than the few dollars it would get at auction.
    syn: worthless; cheap   *ant: valuable*

11. **august** (ô gəst´) *adj.* marked by grandeur and awe
The coronation of the queen was an *august* occasion that was full of pomp and circumstance.
syn: regal; magnificent   *ant: pedestrian; common*

12. **semblance** (sem´ bləns) *n.* an outward likeness in form or appearance
The suspect's alibi was only a partial *semblance* of the truth.
syn: similarity; copy

13. **martyr** (mär´ tər) *n.* one who suffers or sacrifices for a cause
Martin Luther King became a *martyr* for the civil rights movement when an assassin killed him.

14. **dossier** (dôs´ yā) *n.* a file of detailed information on a person or subject
The police had a large *dossier* on the man accused of the theft.
syn: record

15. **conduit** (kän´ dōō ət) *n.* a means by which something is transmitted
The telephone wire must be plugged into the *conduit* for the computer to connect to the Internet.
syn: channel

Exercise I

Words in Context

From the list below, supply the words needed to complete the paragraph. Some words will not be used.

dossier	semblance	picayune	albeit
august	indefatigable	philatelist	behest

1. Like many residents of Crystal Point, Janine walked to the beach every evening to witness the _____ beauty of the sun setting over the Pacific. The white dunes were the best place to experience the beautiful event, _____ several barges on the horizon diminished the view. They were a[n] _____ detail to Janine; it would require more than a few dots on the horizon to distract her from the blazing sky. Today, as Janine approached the water, she was amused to find a large mound of sand in the vague _____ of a whale. The Williards must have visited the beach; they have three _____ children who readily spend entire days creating sand sculptures.

From the list below, supply the words needed to complete the paragraph. Some words will not be used.

asinine	conduit	osmosis	august
autodidact	indiscretion	behest	

2. Alicia knew that it was _____ to wait until the night before the deadline to write her term paper. Her teacher had accepted a late paper in the past, but Alicia recognized that such _____ would not be ignored this time because it was the end of the grading period.

    Luckily for her, Alicia was a[n] _____ who spent her free time reading about the subject of her paper. Having parents who were experts in the field also helped; raised by two historians, Alicia had learned more about history through _____ than she could ever hope to acquire in a classroom.

From the list below, supply the words needed to complete the paragraph. Some words will not be used.

conduit	semblance	dossier	philatelist
ancillary	behest	martyr	

3. At the FBI Director's _____, Special Agent Ford compiled a[n] _____ on Caroline Polk, including a list of charges, previous warrants, and a psychological profile. No, it was not every day that a stamp thief made it to the most-wanted list, but Polk had simply gone too far when she burglarized the stamp collection of Terry Moore, a well-known _____ and, more important, a United States senator. Identifying the suspect had taken only hours; thanks to some _____ guidance from the local police department's homicide unit, investigators found Polk's fingerprints all over the heating _____ that she used to enter the senator's house. Polk's fingerprints were on record, largely because she was the only person in the country currently wanted for the grand theft of precious stamps. The Bureau had declined to arrest Polk in the past, for she was known to be armed, and few agents were willing to become _____ to the cause of stamp collecting.

Exercise II

Sentence Completion

Complete the sentence in a way that shows you understand the meaning of the italicized vocabulary word.

1. "Your *dossier* reads like a novel," said Dr. Isano as he…

2. The weather was sunny and clear, *albeit*…

3. Audrey's *asinine* decision to put foil in the microwave resulted in…

4. Your concerns are too *picayune* for me to…

5. As if by *osmosis*, the rambunctious hockey fans turned the docile Freddy…

6. If the hospital suffers a blackout, *ancillary* services are…

7. Phoebe felt out of place at the *august* induction ceremony because…

8. Ursula was reminded of her past *indiscretions* every time she…

9. The broken underground gas *conduit* caused a mass…

10. Thanks to four cups of coffee, the *indefatigable* Elizabeth can finish…

11. The shoddy reality show didn't bear any *semblance* to…

12. Ivan was brave, but becoming a *martyr* was…

13. The highlight of the *philatelist's* collection is a…

14. At the Admiral's *behest*, Petty Officer Young gave the order to…

15. Living far from civilization and schools, the *autodidact* had to…

Exercise III

Roots, Prefixes, and Suffixes

Study the entries and answer the questions that follow.

The roots *cap*, *capt*, *cept*, and *cip* mean "to take" or "to seize."
The roots *grad* and *gress* mean "step" or "to go."
The prefix *inter–* means "between," "among," or "in the presence of."

1. Using *literal* translations as guidance, define the following words without using a dictionary:

    A. regress   D. precept
    B. degrade   E. captivate
    C. digress   F. capacious

2. Police will use their cars to _____ a driver who flees the scene of a crime.

    If the prefix *e–* means "out," then the literal translation for *egress* is _____.

3. The root *mit* means "to send." What is the appropriate word to describe a radio signal that fades in and out, causing periods of silence between audible transmissions? The root *rog* means "to ask." What would you call a formal questioning of someone who is present and expected to answer the questions?

4. List all the words you can think of that contain the roots *cap*, *capt*, *cip*, or *cept*.

5. List all the words you can think of that begin with the prefix *inter–*.

Exercise IV

Inference

Complete the sentences by inferring information about the italicized word from its context.

1. If the *autodidact* did not have access to a library, she might not…

2. The FBI might compile a *dossier* on someone who…

3. Since the *ancillary* forces failed to arrive in time, the battalion defending the fort…

> ## Exercise V

Writing

Here is a writing prompt similar to the one you will find on the writing portion of an assessment test.

Plan and write an essay based on the following statement:

> "Those who write clearly have readers, those who write obscurely have commentators."
>
> –Albert Camus

Assignment: Write an essay in which you explain what Camus means. Discuss his attitude toward writers and readers, and then, using evidence from your reading, your studies, and your observations, illustrate your opinion of his assertion.

Thesis: Write a *one-sentence* response to the above assignment. Make certain this single sentence offers a clear statement of your position.

> *Example: Albert Camus asserts that writers create certain types of readers, but in reality, each reader has a unique response that is not wholly determined by the clarity or the obscurity of the writing.*

_____

_____

Organizational Plan: List at least three subtopics you will use to support your main idea. This list is your outline.

1. _____

2. _____

3. _____

Draft: Following your outline, write a good first draft of your essay. Remember to support all your points with examples, facts, references to reading, etc.

Review and Revise: Exchange essays with a classmate. Using the Holistic scoring guide on page 262, score your partner's essay (while her or she scores yours). If necessary, rewrite your essay to correct the problems noted by your partner.

Exercise VI

English Practice

Identifying Sentence Errors

Identify the grammatical error in each of the following sentences. If the sentence contains no error, select answer choice E.

1. Only a few stars were visible last night, because there was a full moon.   No error
       (A)   (B)   (C)   (D)   (E)

2. By the time the hail started, we had already ran into the library.   No error
                      (A)   (B)   (C)   (D)   (E)

3. Radio stations aired the story about the miracle operation that restored
                    (A)   (B)
    sight to a blind man in every region of the country.   No error
         (C)   (D)   (E)

4. Jane was already for the prom one hour before her date arrived.   No error
                 (A)   (B)   (C)   (D)   (E)

5. The university registrar is responsible for scheduling office staff, coordinating the
           (A)   (B)
    directory of classes and examinations, and assigning classroom facilities.   No error
           (C)   (D)   (E)

Improving Sentences

The underlined portion of each sentence below contains some flaw. Select the answer choice that best corrects the flaw.

6. Julie added water to the stew, and then it simmered for 20 minutes before she served it.
    A.   which simmered
    B.   simmered
    C.   before it simmered
    D.   simmered and stirred
    E.   and then she was able to simmer the both of them

7. On Christmas morning, the children had almost opened all their gifts by 6 am.
    A.   had opened almost all their gifts
    B.   had almost unwrapped all their gifts
    C.   had unwrapped all their gifts
    D.   had almost opened some presents
    E.   had opened all their gifts

8. New research shows that high I.Q. scores are the result of <u>heredity and also an intellectually stimulating environment</u>.
   A. heredity and an intellectually stimulating environment.
   B. heredity and environments that are intellectually stimulating.
   C. genes and also intellectual stimulation.
   D. genes and environment.
   E. heredity and also environmental causes.

9. <u>Mary told Ellen that she would need</u> a new outfit to wear to the job interview.
   A. Mary told herself that she would need
   B. Mary told Ellen that she needed
   C. Mary told Ellen that she was going to need
   D. Mary told Ellen, "You will need…"
   E. Mary did not tell Ellen that she would need

10. Neither Anthony nor Rose <u>are people who like the beach.</u>
    A. are people whom like the beach.
    B. is a person who like the beach.
    C. is a person who likes the beach.
    D. are people who likes the beach.
    E. is someone who like the beach.

Review Lessons 19-21

Exercise I

Inferences

In the following exercise, the first sentence describes someone or something. Infer information from the first sentence, and then choose the word from the Word Bank that best completes the second sentence.

stipulate	conduit	dissident	demur
burgeon	arbiter	indiscretion	ruminate

1. Max was very good at calming people down before fights broke out, and usually, the people he spoke to walked away with no hard feelings.

   From this sentence, we can infer that Max is a[n] natural _____, who is good at keeping the peace.

2. After a long, troubled week at school, Heather simply wanted to go to her quiet place in the forest and spend the day putting all her thoughts in order.

   From this sentence, we can infer that Heather likes to _____ in her quiet place.

3. The only way to get to the popular beach is to take Sunrise Drive, a two-lane toll road lined with gift shops, overpriced restaurants, and the only gas station for thirty miles.

   From this sentence, we can infer that businesses in the resort town take advantage of the road as the only _____ to the beach.

4. Because he forgot, during his interview, to mention a petty crime he had committed when he was a teenager, Doug failed to pass the background check to become a federal investigator.

   From this sentence, we can infer that even a slight _____ on a criminal record can interfere with career plans much later in life.

5. All the kids looked away and frowned when Dad asked, "Who wants to go running with me at sunrise?"

   From this sentence, we can infer that the kids _____ at the idea of going for a run at dawn.

Exercise II

Related Words

Some of the vocabulary words from Lessons 19 through 21 have related meanings. Complete the following sentences by choosing the word that best fits the context, based on information you infer from the use of the italicized word. Some word pairs will be antonyms, some will be synonyms, and some will simply be words often used in the same context.

1. The _____ had an education *commensurate* with that of a doctor of philosophy in the field of education, though he held no official credentials or diploma.
   A. arbiter
   B. archetype
   C. autodidact
   D. coup
   E. accolade

2. If the deadly virus were allowed to *proliferate* unchecked, the rate of transmission would _____ out of control throughout the civilized world in a matter of days.
   A. stipulate
   B. burgeon
   C. behest
   D. commensurate
   E. ruminate

3. Christmas trees have both religious and *secular* significance, notably as a[n] _____ of the ancient tradition of displaying evergreens as symbols of life amid the bleakness of winter.
   A. archetype
   B. approbation
   C. confluence
   D. conduit
   E. derivative

4. The *arbiter* deciding who should pay for the ruined machinery requested a few hours to _____ over the evidence presented by both sides of the conflict.
   A. proliferate
   B. stipulate
   C. burgeon
   D. ruminate
   E. commensurate

5. The ruthless antagonist of the story bears a[n] _____ to the evil characters that have been included in many previous stories, which makes him easily classifiable as representing the devil *archetype*.
    A. accolade
    B. attrition
    C. semblance
    D. autodidact
    E. confluence

6. The *vacuous* man with a high tolerance for pain lucked out by meeting a film producer who wanted to make movies of someone who injures himself by performing _____ stunts.
    A. ancillary
    B. asinine
    C. belligerent
    D. fixed
    E. insouciant

7. The large campus was a[n] _____of cultural and academic thought from everywhere in the world, and as such, it was a good place to observe the *zeitgeist* of a given year.
    A. confluence
    B. coup
    C. martyr
    D. osmosis
    E. arbiter

8. The _____ of the scout troop are intended to help members deal with the many *vagaries* of wilderness survival.
    A. attrition
    B. tenets
    C. accolade
    D. derivative
    E. archetype

9. Uncle Keith maintained a *vigilant* watch over all the fishing lines, while his _____ nieces and nephews chased salamanders and poked sticks into the muddy banks of the river.
    A. secular
    B. belligerent
    C. insouciant
    D. fixed
    E. asinine

10. The _____ gathered secretly for months while planning their *coup* to overthrow the territorial governor, who had slowly become a tyrant.
    A. autodidacts
    B. conduits
    C. martyrs
    D. dissidents
    E. arbiters

Exercise III

Deeper Meanings

Choose a word to replace the italicized word in each sentence. All of the possible choices for each sentence have similar definitions, but the correct answer will have a connotation that best suits the context. For example, the words "delete," "destroy," and "obliterate" all mean "to remove or wipe out," but no one would ever say, "I destroyed the name from the document." The correct choice will be the word that has the best specific meaning and does not render the sentence awkward in tone or content. When choices seem close, look for a clue in the context that makes one choice better than the other.

Note that the correct answer is not always the primary vocabulary word from the lesson.

sins	blessing	scenarios	belligerent
approbation	coup	dumb	crimes
vacuous	teamwork	hostile	takeover

1. Without the *agreement* of the local chamber of commerce, new stores will not be able to obtain business licenses in the small town.

    Better word: _____

2. The massive corporation purchased the smaller company, and the first phase of the *rebellion* involved the firing of three hundred unnecessary employees.

    Better word: _____

3. Some video games challenge players mentally, while other so-called games are simply *stupid* busywork for the purpose of thoughtlessly wasting time.

    Better word: _____

4. When they arrived at the scene of the fight, the town police searched for the *enraged* people who had started the whole thing.

    Better word: _____

5. The number of violent *indiscretions* in the city increased sharply when the especially addictive new drug hit the streets.

    Better word: _____

Exercise IV

Crossword Puzzle

Use the clues to complete the crossword puzzle. The answers consist of vocabulary words from Lessons 19 through 21.

Across

4. like a wooden nickel
8. person who gets in the middle
10. person seen everywhere
12. all Pomp and Circumstance
14. the national mood
16. pipeline
17. what might happen
18. attach a string

Down

1. to play over and over again
2. like salad in a jungle
3. got the boss's nod
5. like marathon runners
6. picking fights
7. a little sin
9. approver of stamps
11. how water looks best
13. keeping an eye on everything
15. out with the old boss, in with the new

Exercise V

Subject Prompts

Here is a writing prompt similar to the one you will find on the writing portion of an assessment test. Follow the instructions below and write a brief, efficient essay.

The traditional design of a school classroom has been the subject of jokes for decades, especially in the context of aging schools built with salmon-pink hallways leading to pale, drab classrooms. Critics claim that such schools are counterproductive to learning anything— that the color schemes and prison-like atmosphere practically declare failure. Architects traditionally design schools to ensure the efficient flow of people, but are schools ever built to help students think?

Imagine you are an architect who has the opportunity to design a new high school for a district that has a total of 800 students (200 per graduating class). Choose a few key characteristics of your school and explain why the designs would be beneficial to students, and more conducive to learning than your present, real school setting. For your recommendation, consider the places where you personally read, write, study, and communicate most effectively.

Thesis: Write a *one-sentence* response to the above assignment. Make certain this single sentence offers a clear statement of your position.

Example: Schools should be designed to emulate environments in which the present generation truly feels interested and curious, such as among ancient ruins or scenic vistas.

_____

_____

Organizational Plan: List at least three subtopics you will use to support your main idea. This list is your outline.

1. _____

2. _____

3. _____

Draft: Following your outline, write a good first draft of your essay. Remember to support all your points with examples, facts, references to reading, etc.

Review and Revise: Exchange essays with a classmate. Using the scoring guide for Development on page 258, score your partner's essay (while he or she scores yours). Focus on the development of ideas and the use of language conventions. If necessary, rewrite your essay to incorporate more (or more relevant) support and/or improve your use of language.

Scoring Guide for Writing

Organization

6 = Clearly Competent

The paper is **clearly** organized **around the central point or main idea**. The organization may grow from the writer's argument or a slightly predictable structure. Ideas follow a logical order.

The work is **free of surface errors** (grammar, spelling, punctuation, etc.).

5 = Reasonably Competent

The organization of the paper is **clear, but not fully implemented**. The structure might be predictable. Ideas follow a logical order, but transitions might be simple or obvious.

Minor surface errors are present, but they **do not interfere** with the reader's understanding of the work.

4 = Adequately Competent

The organization of the paper is **apparent, but not consistently implemented**. The structure is predictable. Some ideas follow a logical order, but transitions are simple and obvious.

Surface errors are present, but they **do not severely interfere** with the reader's understanding.

3 = Nearly Competent

There is **evidence of a** simple organizational **plan**. Ideas are grouped logically in parts of the paper, but do not flow logically throughout. Transitions are needed.

Surface errors are **apparent** and **begin to interfere** with the reader's understanding of the work.

2 = Marginally Incompetent

The organizational plan of the paper is **obscured by too few details** and/or **irrelevant details**. Some of the ideas are grouped logically in parts of the paper. Transitions are needed or are incorrect.

Surface errors are **frequent and severe enough** to **interfere** with the reader's understanding of the work.

1 = Incompetent

There is **no** clear organizational **plan** and/or **insufficient material**. Ideas are not grouped logically. Transitions are absent.

Surface errors are **frequent** and **extreme**, and **severely interfere** with the reader's understanding of the work.

Scoring Guide for Writing

Development

6 = **Clearly Competent**
The **paper takes a position** on the issue and **offers sufficient material** (details, examples, anecdotes, supporting facts, etc.) to create a **complete discussion**. **Every word and sentence is relevant**. Ideas are **fully supported**.
The paper visits **different perspectives** of the argument or addresses **counterarguments** to the writer's position. The paper **focuses** on the argument evoked by the prompt. There is a **clear**, **purposed**, well-developed **introduction** and **conclusion**.
The work is **free of surface errors** (grammar, spelling, punctuation, etc.).

5 = **Reasonably Competent**
The essay **takes a position** on the issue and **offers sufficient material** for a complete discussion, but the reader is left **with a few unanswered questions**. Ideas are **supported**. The paper **partially visits different perspectives** of the argument or addresses **counterarguments**. **Most** of the paper **focuses** on the argument evoked by the prompt. There is **no irrelevant material**. There is a clear **introduction** and **conclusion**.
Minor surface errors are present, but they **do not interfere** with the reader's understanding of the work.

4 = **Adequately Competent**
The paper **takes a position** on the issue but **does not provide** enough details, examples, or supporting facts for a complete discussion, leaving a **few unanswered questions**. The paper includes **some attention** to **counterarguments** and differing perspectives. **Irrelevant material** is present. **Most** of the paper **focuses** on the topic and the specific argument.
Surface errors are present, but they **do not severely interfere** with the reader's understanding.

3 = **Nearly Competent**
The essay **takes a position** on the issue but **does not include** sufficient details, examples, or supporting facts for a discussion. The paper **may include incomplete or unclear counterarguments**. The paper **might repeat** details or rhetoric. The paper focuses on the topic, but **does not maintain** the specific argument.
Surface errors are **apparent** and **begin to interfere** with the reader's understanding of the work.

2 = **Marginally Incompetent**

The paper **may not take a position** on the issue, or the paper may take a position but **fail to support** it with sufficient details. Examples and ideas are **vague** and **irrelevant**. The paper might **repeat ideas extensively**. The paper **might maintain focus** on the general topic.

Surface errors are **frequent and severe enough** to **interfere** with the reader's understanding of the work.

1 = **Incompetent**

The paper **might attempt to take a position**, but it **fails to provide** examples, fact, or rhetoric to support the position. The paper may be **repetitious** with **little** or **no focus** on the general topic.

Surface errors are **frequent** and **extreme**, and **severely interfere** with the reader's understanding of the work.

Scoring Guide for Writing

Sentence Formation And Variety

6 = Clearly Competent

Sentences are **varied**, **complete**, and **assist the reader** in the flow of the discussion.

The work is **free of surface errors** (grammar, spelling, punctuation, etc.).

5 = Reasonably Competent

Sentences are **somewhat varied**, **generally correct**, and **do not distract** the reader from the flow of the discussion.

Minor surface errors are present, but they **do not interfere** with the reader's understanding of the work.

4 = Adequately Competent

Some sentences show **variety**, and **most** are **complete** and **generally correct**.

Surface errors are present, but they **do not interfere** with the reader's understanding.

3 = Nearly Competent

Sentences show a **little variety**, but the structure may be **dull**. Sentences are **generally complete** and grammatically correct, but **some errors** distract the reader.

Surface errors are **apparent** and **begin to interfere** with the reader's understanding of the work.

2 = Marginally Incompetent

Sentence Structure is **usually simple. Problems** in **sentence structure** and **grammar** distract the reader and provide **little or no variety.**

Surface errors are **frequent and severe enough** to **interfere** with the reader's understanding of the work.

1 = Incompetent

Sentence structure is **simple, generally erroneous** and **lacks variety**.

Surface errors are **frequent** and **extreme**, and **severely interfere** with the reader's understanding of the work.

Scoring Guide for Writing

Word Choice

6 = Clearly Competent
The essay shows a **good command** of language. Word choice is **specific, clear**, and **vivid**, favoring **powerful nouns** and **verbs** to weaker adjective and adverb phrases. **Clear, specific words** are used, instead of vague, general terms.
The work is **free of surface errors** (grammar, spelling, punctuation, etc.).

5 = Reasonably Competent
Language is **competent**. Word choice is **clear** and **accurate**. Words and phrases are **mostly** vivid, specific, and powerful.
Minor surface errors are present, but they **do not interfere** with the reader's understanding of the work.

4 = Adequately Competent
Language is **adequate**, with **appropriate** word choice. **Most** words and phrases are vivid, specific, and powerful.
Serious surface errors are present, but they **do not interfere** with the reader's understanding.

3 = Nearly Competent
Language shows a **basic control** and word choice is **usually appropriate** but **inconsistent**.
Surface errors are **apparent** and **begin to interfere** with the reader's understanding of the work.

2 = Marginally Incompetent
Word choice is usually **vague**.
Surface errors are **frequent** and **severe enough** to **interfere** with the reader's understanding of the work.

1 = Incompetent
Word choice is **simple, vague**, and **inexact**. The writer makes **no attempt** to choose the best words for the topic, audience, and purpose.
Surface errors are **frequent** and **extreme**, and **severely interfere** with the reader's understanding of the work.

Scoring Guide for Writing

Holistic

6 = Clearly Competent

The paper is **clearly organized** around the central idea. Ideas follow a **logical order**.

The paper **takes a position** on the issue and **offers sufficient material** (details, examples, anecdotes, supporting facts, etc.) to create a complete discussion. There is a **clear**, **purposed**, **well-developed** introduction and conclusion.

The paper visits **different perspectives** of the argument or addresses **counterarguments** to the writer's position.

Sentences are **varied**, **complete**, and **assist the reader** in the flow of the discussion.

The paper shows a **good command** of language. Word choice is **specific**, **clear**, and **vivid**, favoring **powerful nouns** and **verbs** to weaker adjective and adverb phrases.

The work is **free of surface errors** (grammar, spelling, punctuation, etc.).

5 = Reasonably Competent

The organization of the paper is **clear**, but **not fully implemented**. Ideas follow a **logical order**, but transitions **might be simple** or obvious. The structure **might be predictable**.

The paper **takes a position** on the issue and **offers sufficient material** for a complete discussion, but the reader is left with **a few unanswered questions**. There is a clear **introduction** and **conclusion**.

The paper visits **some different perspectives** of the argument or addresses **counterarguments**.

Sentences are **somewhat varied**, **generally correct**, and **do not distract** the reader from the flow of the discussion.

Language is **competent**. Words and phrases are **mostly vivid**, **specific**, and **powerful**.

Minor surface errors are present, but they **do not interfere** with the reader's understanding of the work.

4 = Adequately Competent

The organization of the paper is **apparent**, but **not consistently** implemented. The structure is **predictable**. **Some** ideas follow a **logical order**, but transitions are **simple** and **obvious**. **Most** of the paper **focuses** on the topic and the specific argument.

The paper **takes a position** on the issue, but **does not provide** the details, examples, or supporting facts for a complete discussion, leaving **a few unanswered questions**.

The paper includes **little attention** to counterarguments and differing perspectives.

Irrelevant material is present.

Language is **adequate**, with appropriate word choice. **Most** words and phrases are vivid, specific, and powerful.

Some sentences show **variety**, and **most** are **complete** and **generally correct**.

Surface errors are present, but they **do not interfere** with the reader's understanding.

3 = Nearly Competent

There is **evidence of a simple organizational plan**. The essay **takes a position** on the issue but **does not include** sufficient details, examples, or supporting facts for a discussion. Ideas are **grouped logically** in parts of the paper, **but do not flow** logically throughout. The paper **focuses** on the topic, but **does not maintain** the specific argument.

The paper **may include incomplete** or **unclear** counterarguments.

Language shows a **basic control**, and word choice is **usually appropriate** but **inconsistent**. Sentences show a **little variety**, but the structure may be **dull**.

Sentences are **generally complete** and **grammatically correct**, but some errors **distract** the reader.

The paper might **repeat** details or rhetoric.

Surface errors are **apparent** and **begin to interfere** with the reader's understanding of the work.

2 = Marginally Incompetent

The organizational plan of the paper is **obscured by too few details** and/or **irrelevant details**. The paper **may not take a position** on the issue, or the paper may take a position but **fail to support** it with sufficient details. **Some** of the ideas are **grouped logically** in parts of the paper. The paper **generally maintains focus** on the general topic.

Examples and ideas are **vague** and **irrelevant**.

Sentence structure is **usually simple**. **Problems** in sentence structure and grammar **distract** the reader and provide **little** or **no variety**. **Word choice** is usually **vague**.

The paper might **repeat** ideas **extensively**.

Surface errors are **frequent and severe enough** to **interfere** with the reader's understanding of the work.

1 = Incompetent

There is **no clear organizational plan** and/or **insufficient material**. The paper **might attempt** to **take a position**, but it **fails** to provide examples, fact, or rhetoric to support the position. Ideas are **not grouped logically**.

The paper may be **repetitious** with little or **no focus** on the general topic.

Sentence structure is **simple** and **generally erroneous** and **lacking variety**. Word choice is **simple**, **vague**, and **inexact**. The writer makes **no attempt** to choose the best words for the topic, audience, and purpose.

Surface errors are **frequent** and **extreme**, and **severely interfere** with the reader's understanding of the work.

Relevant State Standards

High School - Grades 9-10

These are only the minimum standards that the product line meets; if these standards seem out of order, they typically go in "keyword" order; from the Language Usage category of standards, to Comprehension, Analysis, Writing, Research/Applied, and Technology/Media categories. Therefore, these standards may be in a different order than the order given by your local Department of Education. Also, if one state standard meets multiple categories, that particular standard is listed the first time it appears, to reduce redundancy. Again, please refer to your local Department of Education for details on the particular standards.

Bias/Validity standards are included, as are Voice/Style standards, as both categories include use of words for different effects on the audience (connotation, denotation, distortion, formality, etc.) and, thus, are logical inclusions.

Depending on the state, standards pertaining to use of dialect and idiomatic expressions might be met by this product. Please refer to your local Department of Education for details.

Notation is as close as possible to the notation given by the Department of Education of the respective state.

States:

Alaska:
R4.1.1-4; R4.4.1-2; R4.5.1; R4.5.2-3; W4 (all); R4.1.5; R4.2.1-2; R4.3.1-4; R4.3.5-6; R4.7.1; R4.9.2; R4.9.1; R4.6.1-4; R4.9.1

Indiana:
10.1.1-4; 10.2.3; 10.3.1; 10.2.1; 10.3.7-8; 10.4 (all); 10.6 (all); 10.5 (all); 10.3.11; 10.7.12; 10.3.12; 10.3.6; 10.3.2; 10.4.10-12

Nebraska (standards set at grade 12):
12.1.1; 12.1.5; 12.1.6

Texas (TEKS section 110.43):
b6 (all); b7 (all); b8B; b11D; b12A; b2 (all); b3 (all); b12B-C; B8D; B9A; B11A, F; B5 (entire)

Virginia:
10.4; 10.3; 10.7; 10.8; 10.3D; 10.9

Common Core State Standards for English Language Arts

Standards	Exercises

Reading Standards for Informational Text

Key Ideas and Details

RI.9-10.1	Cite strong and thorough textual evidence to support analysis of what the text says explicitly as well as inferences drawn from the text.	**Critical Reading: Level One** Lessons: 2, 4, 6, 8, 10, 12, 14, 16, 18, 20
RI.9-10.2	Determine a central idea of a text and analyze its development over the course of the text, including how it emerges and is shaped and refined by specific details; provide an objective summary of the text.	**Critical Reading: Level One** Lessons: 2, 4, 6, 8, 10, 12, 14, 16, 18, 20

Craft and Structure

RI.9-10.4	Determine the meaning of words and phrases as they are used in a text, including figurative, connotative, and technical meanings; analyze the cumulative impact of specific word choices on meaning and tone (e.g., how the language of a court opinion differs from that of a newspaper).	**Critical Reading: Level One** Lessons: 2, 4, 6, 8, 10, 12, 14, 16, 18, 20 **Inference: Level One** Lessons: 1-21
RI.9-10.6	Determine an author's point of view or purpose in a text and analyze how an author uses rhetoric to advance that point of view or purpose.	**Critical Reading: Level One** Lessons: 2, 4, 6, 8, 10, 12, 14, 16, 18, 20

Writing Standards

Text Types and Purposes

W.9-10.1	Write arguments to support claims in an analysis of substantive topics or texts, using valid reasoning and relevant and sufficient evidence.	**Writing: Level One** Lessons: 1, 3, 5, 7, 9, 11, 13, 15, 17, 19, 21
W.9-10.1a	Introduce precise claim(s), distinguish the claim(s) from alternate or opposing claims, and create an organization that establishes clear relationships among claim(s), counterclaims, reasons, and evidence.	**Writing: Level One** Lessons: 1, 3, 5, 7, 9, 11, 13, 15, 17, 19, 21
W.9-10.1b	Develop claim(s) and counterclaims fairly, supplying evidence for each while pointing out the strengths and limitations of both in a manner that anticipates the audience's knowledge level and concerns.	**Writing: Level One** Lessons: 1, 3, 5, 7, 9, 11, 13, 15, 17, 19, 21
W.9-10.1c	Use words, phrases, and clauses to link the major sections of the text, create cohesion, and clarify the relationships between claim(s) and reasons, between reasons and evidence, and between claim(s) and counterclaims.	**Writing: Level One** Lessons: 1, 3, 5, 7, 9, 11, 13, 15, 17, 19, 21

W.9-10.1d	Establish and maintain a formal style and objective tone while attending to the norms and conventions of the discipline in which they are writing.	**Writing: Level One** Lessons: 1, 3, 5, 7, 9, 11, 13, 15, 17, 19, 21
W.9-10.1e	Provide a concluding statement or section that follows from and supports the argument presented.	**Writing: Level One** Lessons: 1, 3, 5, 7, 9, 11, 13, 15, 17, 19, 21
W.9-10.2	Write informative/explanatory texts to examine and convey complex ideas, concepts, and information clearly and accurately through the effective selection, organization, and analysis of content.	**Writing: Level One** Lessons: 1, 3, 5, 7, 9, 11, 13, 15, 17, 19, 21
W.9-10.2a	Introduce a topic; organize complex ideas, concepts, and information to make important connections and distinctions; include formatting (e.g., headings), graphics (e.g., figures, tables), and multimedia when useful to aiding comprehension.	**Writing: Level One** Lessons: 1, 3, 5, 7, 9, 11, 13, 15, 17, 19, 21
W.9-10.2b	Develop the topic with well-chosen, relevant, and sufficient facts, extended definitions, concrete details, quotations, or other information and examples appropriate to the audience's knowledge of the topic.	**Writing: Level One** Lessons: 1, 3, 5, 7, 9, 11, 13, 15, 17, 19, 21
W.9-10.2c	Use appropriate and varied transitions to link the major sections of the text, create cohesion, and clarify the relationships among complex ideas and concepts.	**Writing: Level One** Lessons: 1, 3, 5, 7, 9, 11, 13, 15, 17, 19, 21
W.9-10.2d	Use precise language and domain-specific vocabulary to manage the complexity of the topic.	**Writing: Level One** Lessons: 1, 3, 5, 7, 9, 11, 13, 15, 17, 19, 21
W.9-10.2e	Establish and maintain a formal style and objective tone while attending to the norms and conventions of the discipline in which they are writing.	**Writing: Level One** Lessons: 1, 3, 5, 7, 9, 11, 13, 15, 17, 19, 21
W.9-10.2f	Provide a concluding statement or section that follows from and supports the information or explanation presented (e.g., articulating implications or the significance of the topic).	**Writing: Level One** Lessons: 1, 3, 5, 7, 9, 11, 13, 15, 17, 19, 21

Range of Writing	
W.9-10.10	Write routinely over extended time frames (time for re-search, reflection, and revision) and shorter time frames (a single sitting or a day or two) for a range of tasks, purposes, and audiences.	**Writing: Level One** Lessons: 1, 3, 5, 7, 9, 11, 13, 15, 17, 19, 21

Language Standards

Conventions of Standard English

L.9-10.1a	Demonstrate command of the conventions of standard English grammar and usage when writing or speaking.	**Identifying Sentence Errors: Level One** Lessons: 1, 5, 9, 13, 17, 21 **Improving Sentences: Level One** Lesson: 1, 5, 9, 13, 17, 21 **Improving Paragraphs: Level One** Lesson: 3, 7, 11, 15, 19 **Writing: Level One** Lessons: 1, 3, 5, 7, 9, 11, 13, 15, 17, 19, 21
L.9-10.2	Demonstrate command of the conventions of standard English capitalization, punctuation, and spelling when writing.	**Identifying Sentence Errors: Level One** Lessons: 1, 5, 9, 13, 17, 21 **Improving Sentences: Level One** Lessons: 1, 5, 9, 13, 17, 21 **Improving Paragraphs: Level One** Lessons: 3, 7, 11, 15, 19 **Writing: Level One** Lessons: 1, 3, 5, 7, 9, 11, 13, 15, 17, 19, 21

Vocabulary Acquisition and Use	
L.9-10.4	Determine or clarify the meaning of unknown and multiple-meaning words and phrases based on grades 9–10 reading and content, choosing flexibly from a range of strategies.	**Critical Reading: Level One** Lessons: 1-21
L.9-10.4a	Use context (e.g., the overall meaning of a sentence, paragraph, or text; a word's position or function in a sentence) as a clue to the meaning of a word or phrase.	**Word in Context: Level One** Lessons: 1-21 **Inference: Level One** Lessons: 1-21 **Critical Reading: Level One** Lessons: 1-21
L.9-10.4b	Identify and correctly use patterns of word changes that indicate different meanings or parts of speech (e.g., analyze, analysis, analytical; advocate, advocacy).	**Roots, Prefixes, and Suffixes: Level One** Lessons: 1-21
L.9-10.4d	Verify the preliminary determination of the meaning of a word or phrase (e.g., by checking the inferred meaning in context or in a dictionary).	**Inference: Level One** Lessons: 1-21
L.9-10.5	Demonstrate understanding of figurative language, word relationships, and nuances in word meanings.	**Related Words, Deeper Meaning: Level One** Lessons: 1-3, 4-6, 7-9, 10-12, 13-15, 16-18, 19-21
L.9-10.5b	Analyze nuances in the meaning of words with similar denotations.	**Critical Reading: Level One** Lessons: 2, 4, 6, 8, 10, 12, 14, 16, 18, 20
L.9-10.6	Acquire and use accurately general academic and domain-specific words and phrases, sufficient for reading, writing, speaking, and listening at the college and career readiness level; demonstrate independence in gathering vocabulary knowledge when considering a word or phrase important to comprehension or expression.	**Level One:** Lessons: 1-21

History/Social Studies

Key Ideas and Details

RH.9-10.1.	Cite specific textual evidence to support analysis of primary and secondary sources, attending to such features as the date and origin of the information.	**Critical Reading: Level One** Lessons: 2, 4, 6, 8, 10, 12, 14, 16, 18, 20

Craft and Structure

RH.9-10.4	Determine the meaning of words and phrases as they are used in a text, including vocabulary describing political, social, or economic aspects of history/social science.	**Critical Reading: Level One** Lessons: 2, 4, 6, 8, 10, 12, 14, 16, 18, 20
RH.9-10.6	Compare the point of view of two or more authors for how they treat the same or similar topics, including which details they include and emphasize in their respective accounts.	**Critical Reading: Level One** Lessons: 4, 8, 12, 16, 20

Integration of Knowledge and Ideas

RH.9-10.9	Compare and contrast treatments of the same topic in several primary and secondary sources.	**Critical Reading: Level One** Lessons: 4, 8, 12, 16, 20